# REVISE EDEXCEL GCSE
# Geography A
## Geographical Foundations
### For the linear specification first teaching 2012
# REVISION GUIDE

Series Consultant: Harry Smith          Author: Anne-Marie Grant

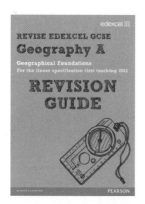

## THE REVISE EDEXCEL SERIES
### Available in print or online

Online editions for all titles in the Revise Edexcel series are available Autumn 2013.

Presented on our ActiveLearn platform, you can view the full book and customise it by adding notes, comments and weblinks.

### Print editions

| | |
|---|---|
| Geography A Revision Guide | 9781446905340 |
| Geography A Revision Workbook | 9781446905357 |

### Online editions

| | |
|---|---|
| Geography A Revision Guide | 9781446905494 |
| Geography A Revision Workbook | 9781446905470 |

Print and online editions are also available for Geography B.

This Revision Guide is designed to complement your classroom and home learning, and to help prepare you for the exam. It does not include all the content and skills needed for the complete course. It is designed to work in combination with Edexcel's main GCSE Geography A 2009 Series.

**To find out more visit:**
www.pearsonschools.co.uk/edexcelgcsegeographyrevision

ALWAYS LEARNING                                    **PEARSON**

# Contents

☑ Make sure you know which topics you have studied – you only need to revise these.

## A small bit of small print
Edexcel publishes Sample Assessment Material and the Specification on its website. This is the official content and this book should be used in conjunction with it. The questions in *Now try this* have been written to help you practise every topic in the book. Remember: the real exam questions may not look like this.

**Target grade ranges**
Target grade ranges are quoted in this book for some of the questions. Students targeting this grade range should be aiming to get most of the marks available. Students targeting a higher grade should be aiming to get all the marks available.

# Basic geographical skills

You will need to be able to label or annotate photographs, sketches, maps, graphs or diagrams.

## Labelling and annotation

You should use a label to name a feature on a photograph. Use annotation to describe or explain something. This photograph has one label and one annotation.

Label

Steep-sided V-shaped valley

Annotation

The fast moving water and the steep landscape cause downwards erosion. This creates V-shaped valleys.

## Types of photography

You need to be able to recognise different types of photography in Geography.

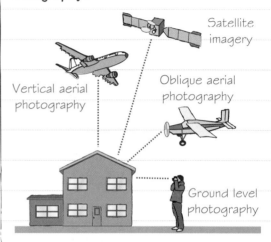

Satellite imagery

Oblique aerial photography

Vertical aerial photography

Ground level photography

---

## Worked example

**C** HIGHER

Look at this OS map extract of Warkworth and Amble.

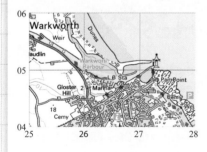

Mark the following on a sketch map:

**1** a tourist feature **(1 mark)**

## Drawing sketches

A sketch:

* can be drawn in the field or from a photograph or a map
* is a simple line drawing
* should be drawn inside a frame
* can be labelled and annotated in the same way as a photograph
* should only include features relevant to the question.

---

## Now try this

**C** FOUNDN

This photograph was taken at grid reference 272049 on the OS map extract in the Worked example above. Mark the location of the lighthouse shown in the photograph with an X on the sketch map above. **(1 mark)**

# Cartographic skills

Atlases provide a variety of information presented graphically or in images. You will need to be able to describe the **distribution** and **patterns** shown on different kinds of maps.

## Atlas maps

One of the most common types of map shows **distribution** – for example, the distribution of vegetation types, such as tropical rainforests.

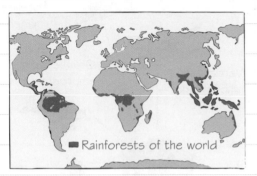

■ Rainforests of the world

Atlases also contain maps which show:

- **climate zones** and global variations in **precipitation** and **rainfall**
- country boundaries (political maps)
- **height** and **shape** of the land (**relief**)
- population distribution (how people are spread within a region or country).

You may be required to use a combination of different types of information to answer a question.

## Describing patterns

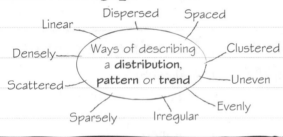

Linear  Dispersed  Spaced

Densely  Ways of describing a distribution, **pattern** or **trend**  Clustered

Scattered  Uneven

Sparsely  Irregular  Evenly

The student has accurately described the **site** and **shape** to get full marks.

### Now try this

HIGHER B

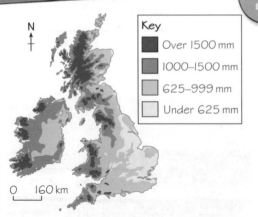

N↑

Key
- ■ Over 1500 mm
- ■ 1000–1500 mm
- ■ 625–999 mm
- □ Under 625 mm

0    160 km

**Describe** the distribution of rainfall shown by the map.    **(5 marks)**

### Worked example

HIGHER B

Find King's Caple in grid square 5628 and grid square 5629. **Describe** the site and shape of King's Caple.    **(4 marks)**

King's Caple has an altitude (height) of 82 m. It is a nucleated settlement as it has grown around a crossroads. The housing is all clustered together. It is also located close to the meander in the River Wye. The settlement is located on a hill and this could have been used for protection or defence.

Don't fall into the trap of **explaining** why the pattern happens. Underline the command word in the question to help you focus your answer.

# Sketch maps

Sketch maps are simple drawings of a place or area. You may need to draw, label or annotate a sketch map for any of the units you study.

## Drawing sketch maps

Sketch maps can be drawn using information from a map or photograph, or drawn in the field, and they:

- show where basic features are located
- have simple labels
- are often drawn from an **aerial** (bird's eye) viewpoint
- are drawn in black and white in exams, but can be in colour for controlled assessment examples
- can be annotated to add more explanation or detailed information.

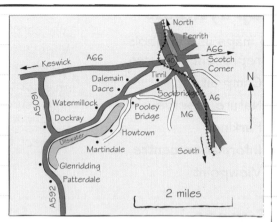

**See also p. 1** For more information on the difference between annotation, labelling and sketching from a photograph.

## Worked example

Look at the OS map extract.

On the sketch map, **draw** the settlement of Langley Park starting in grid reference 2044. **(2 marks)**

Look for the **shape** of the settlement and ensure that you have included it all on your sketch map.

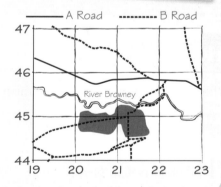

## Now try this

Study the sketch map and the Ordnance Survey map extract from the Worked example above.

1  Complete the table below by adding the correct symbols. **(3 marks)**

| Feature | 4-figure grid reference | Symbol |
|---|---|---|
| Post office | 2345 | |
| Telephone | 2144 | |
| Mast | 1944 | |

2  Locate the features onto the sketch map using the correct symbols. **(3 marks)**

# Map symbols and direction

Accurate use of OS (Ordnance Survey) maps requires important skills, such as using the **key** to identify **symbols**, and use of the compass to work out aspect or direction.

## Map symbols

OS maps use symbols to represent features.

△ Camp site

🐦 Nature reserve

P Parking

ℹ Information centre

☀ Viewpoint

Take care! When answering questions on direction make sure you start from the correct feature!

## Compass points

You may be asked about the **direction** of features from each other.

You will need to learn the **eight** main compass points. All OS maps have a **north** pointed compass.

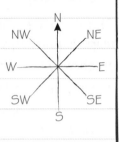

## OS maps

This is an extract from an OS map. There will be a larger OS map extract in the resource booklet provided with your Unit I exam paper.

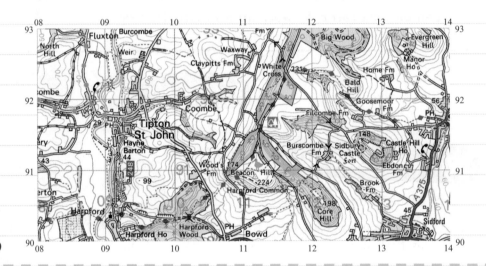

Scale 1:50 000

## Worked example

1  What do the following symbols mean on an OS map?   **(3 marks)**

 Caravan park

PH  Public house (pub)

☀ Viewpoint

2  In the box below, draw the symbol for a battlefield.   **(1 mark)**

Make sure you know what the symbol means by using the key on the OS map.

You do not need to memorise the symbols.

Do not draw symbols too large and always use a **sharp pencil**.

FOUND N **F**

## Now try this

HIGHER **C**

Look at the OS map extract above.

1  What symbol is found at 137913?   **(1 mark)**

2  Which direction is Bald Hill in 1292 from Ebden Farm in 1391?   **(1 mark)**

# Grid references and distances

Grid references are used to locate geographical features on an OS map. You need to know how to use references accurately.

## Grid references

Each line on the map grid has a number. You can use these numbers to locate the features on a map.

You write the distance **along** (from the horizontal **easting** line) before the distance **up** (from the vertical **northing** line). For example, the shaded grid square has a 4-figure grid reference. To find this you would go **along** the corridor (13) then **up** the stairs (02).

The telephone on this map has a 6-figure grid reference 138026.

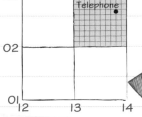

To write a 6-figure grid reference you have to mentally divide each grid square into 10 parts.

## Measuring distance

You will need to work out **distances**. There are two types:

**1** Distances from one point to another in a **linear** fashion are called **straight line** distances – sometimes called 'as the crow flies'.

**2** Distances which follow a **curved** pattern, usually along a river or road, are called **winding** distances.

For the exam you will need a ruler to measure **straight line** distances and a 10 cm piece of string for **winding** distances. The string will be provided for you if it is needed in the exam.

Remember, you will be required to convert the distance measured using the ruler or string into kilometres – use the scale line on the OS map to help you!

## Worked example

HIGHER
C

Look at the OS map extract on page 4.

**1** What is the name of the hill in grid square 1392? **(1 mark)**

Evergreen Hill

**2** What is the 6-figure grid reference of the telephone in 1391? **(1 mark)**

137913

Watch out! A pointer line from the telephone symbol (grid square 1391) shows the **actual** position of the telephone on the main road.

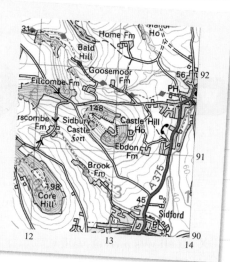

## Now try this

FOUNDN
C

Look at the OS map extract on page 4.

**1** To the nearest kilometre, what is the straight line distance from Brook Farm in grid reference 1290 to Home Farm in grid reference 1392? **(1 mark)**

**2** What type of woodland can be found in grid reference 1192? **(1 mark)**

**3** What is the 6-figure grid reference of the nature reserve near the centre of the map extract? **(1 mark)**

# Cross sections and relief

A visual representation of the landscape from an OS map is called a **cross section**. You may be asked to draw, label or annotate one, or comment on how you would complete it.

## Drawing a cross section

**1** Place a strip of paper along the given transect line.

**2** Mark off the points where the major (brown) contour lines meet the transect line.

**3** Mark the location of other features such as rivers, roads or high points.

**4** With the paper strip lined up with the x-axis, transfer the contour lines to the grid.

**5** Mark off the height of each contour line using a neat cross. Join up the crosses with a ruler and a sharp pencil.

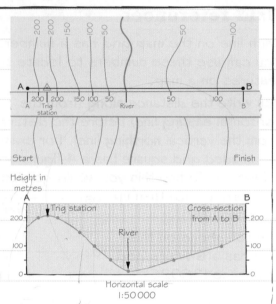

## Slopes

The closer the contours, the steeper the slope!

There are different types of slope:
- **concave** slope.
- **convex** slope.

Look at the OS map extract on the right.

Put a cross in the boxes below to describe the shape of the land from A to B.  **(2 marks)**

☐ The land rises more gently towards the west.
☐ The land at B is the highest.
☒ It shows a river valley.
☒ The land at A is the highest.
☐ The river goes through coniferous forest.

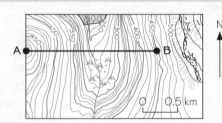

In multiple choice questions look at the number of marks as this is likely to tell you the number of answers required.

Look at the OS extract in the Worked example.

Create a cross section of line A–B.  **(4 marks)**

# Land use and settlement shapes

OS maps show **land use**, **vegetation types**, **communications** and the **shape** of settlements. You may be asked to describe these features.

## OS map features

On an OS map you will find information about:

- land use (settlements and farmland)
- vegetation (woods and parklands)
- communication (roads and railways).

You may need to **describe** the **pattern** or **trend** shown on the map.

The OS map key will help you identify different types of land use.

**See also p. 2**

For more on describing patterns.

## Describing settlements

To **describe** and **identify** settlements remember the 3 Ss:

- **site** – physical characteristics of the place
- **situation** – location in relation to other places
- **shape** – the way the settlement looks from an aerial or 'bird's eye' view.

Remember: SAGA **S**lope (gentle or steep), **A**spect (north, east, south or west facing), **G**round conditions (for example, floodplain), **A**ltitude (height above sea level).

### Settlement shapes

There are three types of settlement shape:

Dispersed

Nucleated

Linear

## Worked example

**FOUND'N D**

Look at the OS map extract.

Find King's Caple in grid square 5628 and grid square 5629.

1 Put a cross in the correct box to describe the shape of King's Caple. **(1 mark)**

[X] nucleated

☐ scattered

☐ dispersed

☐ random

2 Explain your answer to **(1)**. **(2 marks)**

The buildings are grouped around one area, therefore it is nucleated.

## Now try this

**HIGHER C**

Look at the map extract in the Worked example.

Describe the distribution of woodland shown on the map. Use map evidence in your answer. **(4 marks)**

When describing patterns you will need to give map evidence to do well. Use grid references, road or settlement names, distances and directions.

# Physical and human patterns

You may be asked to use photographs, maps or sketches to describe or explain **physical** and **human** patterns. This skill is used throughout all the assessment elements in each unit.

## Describing patterns

You should learn to describe and / or explain the **distribution** and **pattern** of physical features (rivers and coastlines) and human features (settlements and roads).

Use the same technique you would use to describe any other type of pattern.

- You can use maps, photographs and sketches to describe an area.

- You can describe the site of a settlement using a map.

- A photograph or sketch can provide more detail about the **function** of the settlement.

**See also p. 2**

For key words to use when **describing** patterns or **trends**.

## Worked example

**HIGHER B-A**

Describe the section of the River Browney and its valley shown on the map extract. Use map evidence in your answer. **(4 marks)**

There is mixed woodland located to the north of the river. This woodland is 100m above sea level. The river flows through the wood towards the south-east in grid square 1815. The bottom of the valley is approximately 500m wide and there are lots of meanders along the river.

Make sure you use a good range of descriptive comments and map evidence.

## Now try this

Remember to focus on the **human** and **physical** reasons for the growth of the settlement.

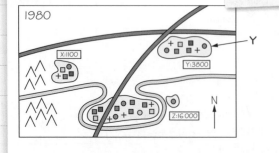
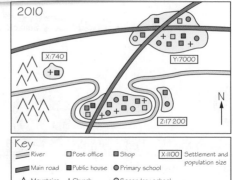

Suggest reasons why Settlement Y has grown. **(3 marks)**

8

Had a look ☐ Nearly there ☐ Nailed it! ☐

GEOGRAPHICAL SKILLS

# Human activity on OS maps

You need to be able to recognise different types of human activity on an OS map. You may be tested on these.

OS maps may show evidence of the following types of human activity:

Industrial (e.g. factories and industrial estates)

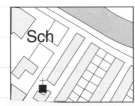

Residential (e.g. houses and flats)

Rural (e.g. forestry and agriculture)

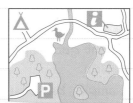

Tourism (e.g. visitor centres and leisure facilities)

## Worked example

Look at the map extract of Ross-on-Wye, a town visited by many tourists.

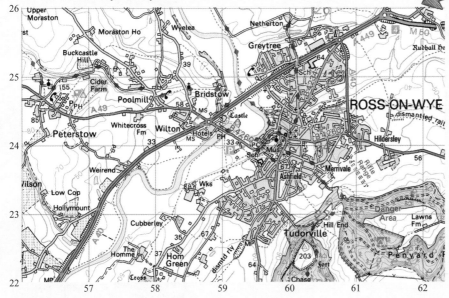

Give **two** pieces of map evidence which show that Ross-on-Wye is visited by tourists. **(2 marks)**

At 568247 there is a camp site and at 596245 there is an information centre.

**EXAM ALERT!**

These questions are often answered incorrectly. Make sure you look at the map carefully.

Students have struggled with exam questions similar to this – **be prepared!**

ResultsPlus

Name **two** tourist attractions you can see on the map. You can give a grid reference for each one, to show that you know where they are.

## Now try this

The town of Ross-on-Wye is very popular with tourists. Use the OS map extract above to complete the table with **two** more tourist facilities and their symbols. One has already been done for you. **(2 marks)**

| Tourist facility | Symbol |
|---|---|
| Car park | P |
| Campsite | ⌂ ⅄ |
| information site | i |

You need to include the **name** of the facility **and** the appropriate **symbol**.

9

# Graphical skills

Graphs and charts show geographical information in a visual way. You may need to use these in any of the units.

## Presenting information

Different types of graphs and charts are used to present geographical information.

For example, bar charts are used to compare a number of different categories, such as types of buildings: offices, shops, houses, factories.

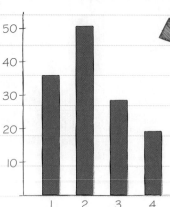

Make sure you choose the right kind of graph or chart for the data you want to present.

Information may also be presented in any of the following ways:

- line graphs
- pie charts
- scatter graphs
- compound graphs
- pictograms.

## Practise!

In an exam question you may be asked to do any of the following:

- **Complete** an 'unfinished' graph or chart using data supplied.
- **Describe** the trend or pattern shown – often by using 'evidence' or 'data'.
- **Explain** the data shown.
- **Suggest** a particular graphical technique you would use to represent a data set.
- **Justify** why a certain graphical technique would be more appropriate than others.

Make sure you have practised each of these.

## Worked example

Complete the population graph for Warkworth and England. Use the data in the table below. **(2 marks)**

| Age | 10–19 |
|-----|-------|
| Warkworth | 5 |
| England | 9 |

Most graphs will have been partly completed for you. Make sure you are **accurate** when drawing the bars, using a **sharp pencil** and a **ruler**.

Remember – if the graph is shaded, then you should shade your completed sectors too.

## Now try this

The population graph in the Worked example above compares the population structure of the town of Warkworth with that of England.

Comment on the age structure of Warkworth compared to England. Use population data in your answer. **(4 marks)**

Remember to include data from the graph in your answer. This could be in the form of years or population figures. Also try to use a 'comparison' word such as 'whereas'.

# Geographical investigation

An enquiry is a step-by-step **investigation** which focuses on a task question, using **primary** and **secondary sources**. You will need to know about geographical investigation and enquiry.

## Enquiry steps

Your geographical investigation or enquiry should follow a logical step-by-step process.

**Step 1**
Identify the geographical **question** or **issue** you are investigating and create sub-questions to help you answer it.

**Step 2**
Establish a **sequence** of investigation.

**Step 3**
**Extract** information from a range of sources (field observations, maps, drawings, photographs, diagrams, tables and secondary sources). You will then need to **present** the information.

**Step 4**
**Describe** (label any pattern or trends), Analyse and interpret (suggest reasons to explain) your evidence.

**Step 5**
Draw a **conclusion** and **justify** it using the evidence you have collected.

**Step 6**
Evaluate the investigation – including the methods used to collect data, and the presentation and analysis of the evidence.

## ICT

ICT can be helpful in your geographical investigation in the following ways:

- websites for research
- software packages to help write up your enquiry, e.g. GIS (Geographical Information Systems)
- to help you present data using layering techniques and a combination of Excel and Google Maps, or dedicated software such as Aegis.

---

## Worked example

Describe **one** way that ICT can be used to prepare for fieldwork **or** to collect fieldwork data. **(3 marks)**

A GIS map is made using ICT. This allows you to choose which fieldwork data can be layered onto the map and you only need to show the necessary information rather than everything that you would normally have on a map.

---

## Now try this

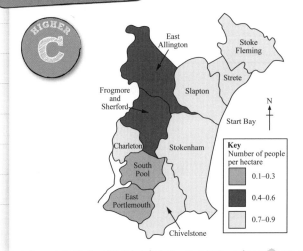

Key
Number of people per hectare

- 0.1–0.3
- 0.4–0.6
- 0.7–0.9

Geographical Information Systems (GIS) can be used to display the population data shown in the choropleth map.

What is meant by the term Geographical Information Systems (GIS)? **(2 marks)**

You need to understand what GIS is and how it can help **illustrate** and interpret data.

# Causes of climate change

Average global temperatures have increased over time. The causes of this increase can be linked to both **natural** and **human** influences. You will need to understand the impact of these influences.

## Natural causes

These are often linked to the development of ice ages throughout geological time.

Natural Causes

Solar output
The amount of energy given off by the Sun.

Orbital geometry (the way the Earth orbits the Sun): Circular orbits result in cold, glacial periods. Elliptical orbits result in warmer periods.

Volcanic eruptions
Mt Laki in 1783 released so much ash that it blocked the Sun.

The Milankovitch mechanism
• variation in Earth's orbit of Sun
• Earth wobbles on axis
• angle of Earth's tilt varies

## Human causes

Over the past forty years there has been concern over how humans are contributing to climate change.

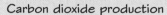

Human causes

Increased wealth has led to demand for energy, food, goods and transport.

Increased car ownership

Increase emissions of greenhouse gases (GHGs)

Carbon dioxide production – rapid increase in the last 100 years from burning of fossil fuels (oil and coal) and car exhausts.

These gases 'trap' solar radiation reflected from the Earth and increase global temperatures. This is known as the **greenhouse effect**.

## Worked example

There has been an increase in the amount of methane being released into the atmosphere.

Suggest reasons for this increase.    **(2 marks)**

Methane has increased because certain countries, such as China, need more food so rice fields have increased and we have more cows. There has also been a change in eating habits due to increasing money to spend so people are now eating more meat and dairy products.

You need to give **two** separate reasons. You do **not** need to **explain** them!

Comment on the increase in the sources of the gas, rather than their effect on the environment.

## Now try this

Using examples, explain **two** other causes of climate change since the last ice age.    **(6 marks)**

# The negative effects of climate change

Climate change will affect the population and the environment. You need to know how and why.

## Impact of climate change

The two main potential impacts of climate change are on **food production** and changes in **sea level**.

Climate change

**Food production**

Crop yields (the amount of food a field can produce) **drops** when temperatures are more or less than the optimum.

↓

Places like USA and Canada will be badly affected as they export 43.7% (2007) of world's wheat.

↓

**Demand** for food will **increase** due to reduced harvests.

↓

**Food price** will **rise** due to scarcity.

↓

Places such as Sub-Saharan Africa will be badly affected with increased cases of malnutrition and famine.

**Sea levels**

Land based ice sheets may melt.

↓

Sea levels could **rise**.

↓

Low-lying land (Bangladesh and the Maldives) most at threat from coastal flooding.

↓

Coastal settlements and farmland could be flooded.

↓

May result in loss of crop harvest, houses being destroyed and potentially lead to increases in diseases.

Other potential impacts include:

- increased incidences of diseases, e.g. malaria
- more frequent tropical storms, e.g. Cyclone Sidr, which affected Bangladesh in November 2007.

## Worked example

Describe two **negative** effects of climate change on the environment. Use examples in your answer. **(4 marks)**

Sea temperatures are getting warmer and this kills sensitive coral reefs by bleaching them – for example, the Great Barrier Reef in Australia.

More dangerous powerful hurricanes and cyclones will form due to warmer sea temperatures.

State the negative effects and give an example.

Remember that place names are proper nouns, so you need to use capital **letters** – for example, **A**ustralia.

## Now try this

Describe how climate change may impact on global food production. Use examples in your answer. **(4 marks)**

It is important that you use **global** examples in your answer.

13

# Responses to climate change

The threat of climate change can be tackled on different scales, from individual action to **international** co-operation. You need to know examples of what action can be taken on these different scales.

## Sustainable living

As individuals, there are ways we can help preserve the environment and take responsibility for the future of our planet:

- Reduce energy waste – turn down heating thermostats; install double glazing, loft and wall insulation.

- Buy local produce.

- Practise the 3 R's – Reduce, Reuse, Recycle.

- Use a car less – walk or cycle instead.

- Save water – use a 'hippo' in your cistern and a water butt for the garden.

**National campaigns** can help raise awareness, but **conflict** can occur – between **economic growth** and **conservation** of the planet!

## Attitudes to climate change

Governments are trying to reduce the rate of climate change. Several world conferences have been held to discuss these issues, but not all countries agree to make changes.

**1988** UN set up IPCC – 1st report showed Earth had warmed by 0.5°C in last 100 years

**1997** Kyoto Protocol

**2009** Copenhagen Accord

**1992** Rio Earth Summit

**2007** Bali

**2011** Durban, S. Africa

There is no agreement on the following important issues.

- Is climate change still occurring now?

- Are the causes of climate change human or natural?

- Should we respond to climate change globally, nationally, locally or individually?

Opinion on climate change depends on **attitudes** or beliefs, which can be influenced by the **media** and influential stakeholders.

## Worked example

Describe **one** local response to climate change.    **(3 marks)**

On the Danish island of Samsø, residents are attempting to become carbon neutral. They have introduced 11 wind turbines which generate 28 000 MWs of electricity. They create so much that they sell 10% of it to Denmark. This is a renewable form of energy and therefore no greenhouse gas emissions are given off, so it helps to reduce climate change.

Remember to link your local response to how it helps **reduce** climate change. The use of a case study or example will help you do well.

## Now try this

Climate change needs to be tackled at various levels. Describe why it can be difficult to implement changes at an international level.

**(3 marks)**

Remember to focus on the correct **scale** of the problem – international. What can governments do to help reduce climate change?

# Sustainable development

Sustainable development is 'development that meets the needs of the present without **compromising** (limiting) the ability of future generations to meet their own needs'. Individuals, governments and organisations have different definitions for the term, these are influenced by their values and attitudes.

## Large companies

Companies must ensure that they make a profit and keep their shareholders happy. However, they can also help **conserve** the environment as part of their business practices.

Changing the culture – improving lives of stakeholders

Eliminating waste

Interface Inc (the largest manufacturer of commercial carpets in USA) helps to conserve the environment by:

Removing toxic substances

Redesigning processes and products

Resourcing efficient transport

Creating new business models that include sustainability

Using renewable energy

## Sustainable transport schemes

Increased transport in urban areas has a negative **impact** on the environment.

There are different ways in which congestion and pollution can be reduced.

- Park and Ride schemes (Oxford, Cheltenham)
- Cycle lanes (Brighton, London)
- Congestion charging (London)
- Improving public transport (Super trams in Sheffield)
- Encouraging car sharing (Milton Keynes)
- Widening roads to allow more traffic
- Ring roads and bypasses to keep through-traffic out of city centres.

Park-and-ride schemes can reduce traffic congestion in city centres.

## Public versus private debate

Public transport will always be more efficient and sustainable than private transport. However, this is easier to achieve in high density cities such as London where everything is close together, as opposed to large, US cities such as Houston.

## Worked example

**D**

State **two** reasons why cities like Durham have introduced congestion charging. **(2 marks)**

More people will use public transport such as buses or even walk.

There will be fewer cars in the city centre, so people can walk around easier.

## Now try this

**C**

Using examples, discuss some ways in which traffic can be managed sustainably. **(9 marks + 4 marks SpaG)**

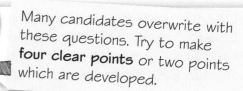

Many candidates overwrite with these questions. Try to make **four clear points** or two points which are developed.

# Sustainable development: tropical rainforests

Many areas of tropical rainforest (TRF) are exploited for their natural resources. This impacts on the environment, people and the economy.

## Case study

You need to know a range of examples of resource extraction and contrasting management initiatives.

## Oil extraction

### Oriente in Ecuador
First developed in 1972 by multinational corporations such as Texaco.

### Effects
- Toxic waste or oil spillages may be discharged into water supplies (e.g. 4.3 million gallons daily).
- Companies are often foreign owned, and any profits go abroad. There is limited money available to improve local living standards.
- Loss of biodiversity as habitats are destroyed and species endangered.
- Extraction by-products such as waste sulphur and oil sludge from storage pits, can cause environmental damage.

### Management initiatives
- 👍 Preservation areas set up, e.g. Limonchocha National Biological Reserve
- 👍 A new constitution in 1998 meant people had to be consulted on development in the TRF.
- 👍 Education initiatives, e.g. ecotourism rainforest exhibitions such as Yasuni National Park.
- 👍 Replanting areas to re-establish habitats.

## Palm oil plantations for biofuel use

### Papua New Guinea (PNG)
There are four major palm oil plantations in PNG and it is now the country's largest agricultural foreign exchange earner, overtaking coffee.

### Effects
- A move away from traditional land use processes.
- Pollution of water sources during construction and operation.
- Farmers and owners become dependent on the industry, which can cause a problem if the price of palm oil changes.
- Plantations reduce the biodiversity as habitats are destroyed.

### Management initiatives
- 👍 Introduction of **ecotourism**.
- 👍 Selling of local produce to benefit local economy (such as Galip nuts).
- 👍 Educating main importers on the need to protect tropical forests.

Debt: some schemes allow debt to richer countries to be **swapped** for rainforest conservation.

## Worked example (HIGHER C)

Outline **one** effect of resource extraction on the environment in tropical rainforest areas.
**(2 marks)**

Oil extraction in the tropical rainforests of Ecuador has resulted in high concentrations of toxic waste (hydrocarbons) in the river water. This has killed aquatic plants and animals.

## Now try this (FOUNDN C)

Using examples, explain how the impacts of resource extraction from tropical rainforest areas are being managed.
**(6 marks + 4 marks SPaG)**

Make sure you read the question carefully. Only impacts on the environment are required.

# Types of waves

Waves can be **constructive** and **destructive**. You will need to know the features of both types of wave, and how they are formed.

## How waves form

Waves form due to a transfer of **energy** and the action of the **wind**. The energy of a wave depends on:

- the distance the wind has been blowing
- the speed the wind is travelling
- the length of time the wind has been blowing.

These factors determine whether a wave is constructive or destructive.

As wind travels over the sea there is a **transfer** of **energy**

Direction of the prevailing wind

The top of the wave is not slowed by friction, and the wave breaks

Energy transfer results in friction, causing the sea to move in a **circular** motion

As the sea becomes shallower near the coast, increased **friction** slows down the base of the wave

## Destructive waves

High wave in proportion to length

A tall breaker. It breaks downwards with great force

Weak swash

Strong backwash

- occur in stormy conditions
- have high energy
- have probably travelled a long distance (large **fetch**)
- are responsible for **erosion**
- have a greater **backwash** than swash.

## Constructive waves

Low wave in proportion to length

Strong swash

Weak backwash

- occur in calm conditions
- have lower energy
- help transport material by **longshore drift**
- are responsible for **deposition**
- have a greater **swash** than backwash.

## Worked example

Label **three** features of a constructive wave on the wave outline shown in Figure 1 opposite.

**(3 marks)**

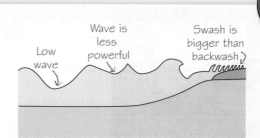

Low wave

Wave is less powerful

Swash is bigger than backwash

Figure 1

## Now try this

Outline the characteristic features of a destructive wave. You may use a diagram in your answer.

**(4 marks)**

If you use a diagram as part of your answer, it should be **annotated** to show the features.

**17**

# Coastal processes and landforms

The coastline is shaped by processes of **weathering** and **erosion** producing different **landforms**. You need to be able to identify these landforms and understand how they are created.

## Coastal processes

**Erosion** helps wear away rock and **removes** the eroded material.

**Weathering** helps wear away rocks but leaves the weathered material **in situ**.

Use the mnemonic 'Annabel can have an apple' to help you remember the erosional processes: **A**brasion; **C**orrosion; **H**ydraulic **a**ction; **A**ttrition.

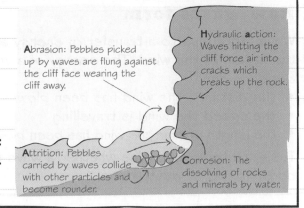

**A**brasion: Pebbles picked up by waves are flung against the cliff face wearing the cliff away.

Hydraulic action: Waves hitting the cliff force air into cracks which breaks up the rock.

Attrition: Pebbles carried by waves collide with other particles and become rounder.

Corrosion: The dissolving of rocks and minerals by water.

## Mass movement

This occurs when large sections of cliff collapse due to weathering. The **two** most common types are:

**1** **Slumping** – The base of the cliff is **eroded** by the sea and the top is saturated with rain. The cliff starts to slide.

**2** **Rock falls** – Fragments of rock break from the cliff face due to weathering, and fall to the base of the cliff.

## Wave-cut platforms

The erosion of cliffs can create wave-cut platforms – areas of flat rock at the base of a cliff.

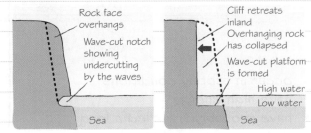

Rock face overhangs

Wave-cut notch showing undercutting by the waves

Sea

Cliff retreats inland

Overhanging rock has collapsed

Wave-cut platform is formed

High water
Low water

Sea

## Worked example

HIGHER C

Study the photograph below.
It shows recession on the Holderness coastline.

What type of mass movement has occurred here? **(1 mark)**

Slumping.

Make sure that you can recognise the different forms of mass movement from photographic evidence.

## Now try this

FOUNDN E

Look at the photo in the Worked example and describe the effects of the mass movement shown.

**(3 marks)**

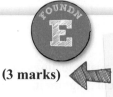

Avoid linking **two** effects together. Try to include **different** ones to get full marks.

# Erosional coastal landforms

Coastal erosion produces distinctive landforms. You should be able to identify these landforms and explain how they are formed.

## Headlands and bays

These landforms develop on coastlines where there is a mixture of hard and soft rock. They often occur where cliffs have fault lines or distinctive joints.

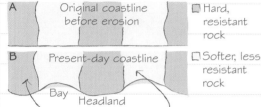

A   Original coastline before erosion    ☐ Hard, resistant rock

B   Present-day coastline    ☐ Softer, less resistant rock

Bay    Headland

Hard or **resistant** rocks such as limestone and chalk take a long time to erode and are often left 'jutting' out into the sea to form **headlands**. For example, Ballard Point, near Swanage

Soft rocks such as gravels, sands and clay are less resistant to erosion and wear away more quickly, to form **bays**. For example, Lulworth Cove, Dorset

## Caves, arches, stacks and stumps

These are formed on coastlines that have harder, more resistant rock.

Cave    Stack    Arch

Stump

---

1   Name landform X in the photograph.    **(1 mark)**

Stump

2   Label two other coastal features on the photograph.    **(2 marks)**

Headland    Stack

X

### EXAM ALERT!

Remember when answering questions like this:

- that the sea is not a landform
- to label the diagram rather than writing your answers under the question
- to draw a line with your label pointing to the feature.

Students have struggled with exam questions similar to this – **be prepared!**

ResultsPlus

---

HIGHER **B**

**Explain** the formation of headlands and bays. You may use a diagram(s) in your answer.    **(4 marks)**

You should **explain** how the landforms develop, not just describe what they look like.

# Depositional landforms 1

The action of the waves can **transport** material from one place to another. The directions of waves and wind can determine the formation of distinctive **depositional** landforms. You will need to understand the processes involved, and how these landforms are created.

## Longshore drift

This is the process by which beach sediment can be **transported** along the coast by waves.

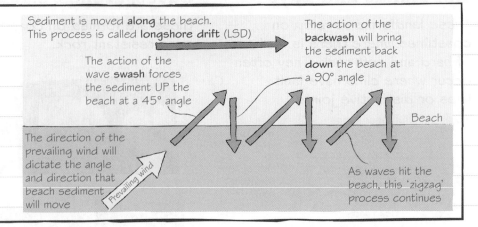

Sediment is moved **along** the beach. This process is called **longshore drift** (LSD)

The action of the wave **swash** forces the sediment UP the beach at a 45° angle

The action of the **backwash** will bring the sediment back **down** the beach at a 90° angle

Beach

The direction of the prevailing wind will dictate the angle and direction that beach sediment will move

Prevailing wind

As waves hit the beach, this 'zigzag' process continues

## Beaches

Once waves lose their energy, they deposit sediment to form beaches. These landforms:

- are formed by **constructive** waves
- consist of eroded material – usually **sand** or **shingle**
- are made up of sediment that will vary in size according to the **geology** of the area and the **energy** of the waves.

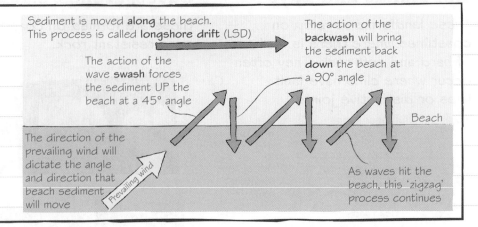

**See also p. 17**

For more on constructive waves.

## Worked example

**F** FOUNDN

Deposition mainly occurs when the

☐ **A** waves have high energy, causing material to be dropped

☒ **B** waves have lower energy, causing material to be dropped

☐ **C** waves remove material from the coastline

☐ **D** wind is mainly blowing offshore          **(1 mark)**

Make sure you read through all the options before you choose what you think is the right answer.

Never leave a question blank – if in doubt take an educated guess!

## Now try this

**A** HIGHER

Study the photo.

Spurn Head is a spit formed by longshore drift.

Describe the process of longshore drift. You may use a diagram to help your answer.          **(3 marks)**.

To answer this question you can use a written explanation or a diagram, or a combination of both is acceptable.

# Depositional landforms 2

Spits and bars are major depositional landforms. You will need to know examples of these landforms, and be able to explain how they are formed.

## How a spit is formed

A spit is an extended stretch of beach material, joined to the mainland, that **projects** out to sea.

## How a bar is formed

A bar is an extended stretch of beach material that grows **across** a **bay**, joining two **headlands**.

## Worked example

Look at the diagram in Box 1.

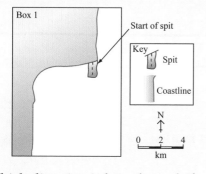

Box 1

Start of spit

Key — Spit

Coastline

N
↑
0   2   4
km

**1** In which direction is longshore drift moving?                    **(1 mark)**

☒ **A** north to south        ☐ **C** east to west

☐ **B** south to north        ☐ **D** west to east

**2** How long is the spit in Box 1?        **(1 mark)**

☐ **A** 1 km        ☐ **C** 3 km

☒ **B** 2 km        ☐ **D** 4 km

**3** In Box 2 draw a labelled diagram to show how the spit would change over time.    **(3 marks)**

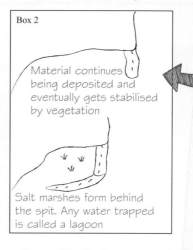

Box 2

Material continues being deposited and eventually gets stabilised by vegetation

Salt marshes form behind the spit. Any water trapped is called a lagoon

Make sure you do what the question asks. Practise drawing landforms so that you are familiar with them.

## Now try this

Describe the formation of a spit. Use a diagram in your answer.        **(4 marks)**

Labelled diagrams can help improve your answer, but don't repeat the same idea in your written answer and on your diagram.

# How coastal landforms change

Cliff erosion causes cliffs to **recede** (or **retreat**). You need to understand how and why this happens and the impact it can have on local people and the environment.

## Factors influencing cliff recession

**1** **Fetch** – a large open body of water will cause a bigger fetch and therefore produce more destructive waves eroding cliffs more easily.

**See also p. 17**
For more about fetch.

**2** **Geology** – harder, more resistant rocks, e.g. granite, will erode more slowly than less resistant rocks, e.g. clay, gravels or sands.

**3** **Coastal management** – coastal defences can help slow down the rate of erosion and protect the coastline.

**See also p. 24**
For more about coastal defences.

Key
☐ Younger, softer rock in the East
■ Harder, older rock in the North West

## Impacts of cliff recession

**1** **Human** – loss of property, e.g. Durlston Bay, Dorset and loss of businesses, e.g. Holbeck Hotel, Yorkshire in 1993. Problems: difficult to get insurance; property prices low.

**2** **Natural** – destruction of habitats for plants and animals, e.g. Durlston Bay is home to 250 species of bird.

---

## Worked example

Explain the factors affecting the rate of coastal recession. **(4 marks)**

Cliff recession is influenced by the distance the wave has travelled. If waves have travelled a great distance, then they cause more erosion. When there is management at the coastline, such as a sea wall or revetment, this will deflect the energy or absorb it. This will mean there is less energy in the wave, so less erosion and therefore cliff recession will be reduced.

Make sure you do **explain** terms here rather than simply **defining** them.

Make sure you give a **reason** (for example, geology) and then apply it to **why** it increases or decreases coastal recession.

---

## Now try this

Explain how variations in the length of **fetch** and the **geology** might increase the rate of coastal recession.
**(4 marks)**

Make sure that you read the question carefully. You must **explain** two variations – one for each of the two factors given in the question.

# Coastal flooding

Many coastal regions are at **risk** from flooding. Make sure you know about the causes of coastal flooding, and how its impact can be reduced.

## Causes

Coastal flooding is caused by:

- high tide levels
- storm surges
- the action of waves – often influenced by wind speed during stormy conditions
- sea level rise – a result of **global warming**, which is causing ice sheets and glaciers to melt, and through **thermal expansion**.

It has been predicted that sea levels will rise by about 0.6 m by the end of the century!

Remember – it is **low-lying** areas, such as Bangladesh, the Maldives, the Netherlands and parts of the Thames Estuary, that are most at risk from coastal flooding.

## Reducing the impact

**Prediction**

- The Environment Agency monitors sea conditions to help predict potential flooding

**Prevention**

- Barriers to protect against high tides, e.g. Thames Barrier
- Areas of open space on flood plains to allow flood water to spill over
- Flood walls built along rivers, e.g. Thames

**Planning**

- Early warning system
- Flood education (what to do in the event of a flood)
- Escape routes, e.g. roofs easily accessible
- Advice from Health Protection Agency on health issues

## Worked example

Outline how the effects of coastal flooding can be reduced. Use examples in your answer. **(4 marks)**

Flooding at the coast can be alleviated by putting in defences such as sea walls and restricting planning permission on the floodplains near to the mouth of the river. London is protected by the Thames Barrier and plans are being made to build more walls along the river. Poorer countries such as Bangladesh cannot afford such engineering and have warning systems so people can move to higher ground and get to safety.

Make sure you use specific facts or examples in your answer, rather than generalised information.

## Now try this

Describe how the effects of coastal flooding can be reduced through prediction and prevention. Use examples in your answer. **(4 marks)**

Make sure you know the difference between **prediction** and **prevention**. You will find this useful for the tectonics topics as well.

# Coastal protection

The UK coastline is protected by **soft** and **hard** engineering. You need to know the advantages and disadvantages of each type.

## Hard engineering

A traditional approach to protecting coasts involves building structures.

Sea wall e.g. Blackpool

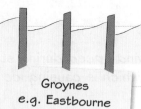

Groynes e.g. Eastbourne

Rip rap e.g. Dawlish Warren

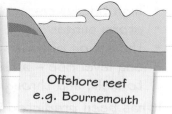

Offshore reef e.g. Bournemouth

👍 Protected cliffs and buildings

👎 Expensive (£5000–£10000 per linear m)

👍 Prevents sea removing sand

👎 Exposes other areas of coastline

👍 Relatively cheap (£2000 per m of timber)

👍 Rocks absorb wave energy

👍 Relatively cheap (£1000–£3000 per m)

👍 Waves break on reef and lose power

👎 Expensive and may interfere with fishing (£5000 per m)

## Soft engineering

This approach looks at factors such as tourism, as well as the nature of the rocks and waves.

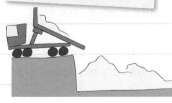

Beach replenishment e.g. Carlyon Bay

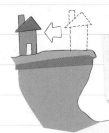

Managed retreat e.g. San Mateo County, California

Cliff regrading e.g. Swanage Bay

👍 Sand reduces wave energy and maintains tourism

👍 Relatively cheap (£2000 per m)

👍 People and activities avoid erosion by moving inland

👎 Expensive as compensation needs to be paid

👍 Reduces slippage

👎 Foot of cliff still needs protection from the waves

## Worked example

FOUND'N D

Beach replenishment is a type of soft engineering.

State **one** advantage of beach replenishment. **(1 mark)**

It is more pleasing to look at as it doesn't involve building ugly structures such as a sea wall (hard engineering).

## Now try this

Choose an area of coast you have studied. Explain how this area of coastline has been managed. **(6 marks)**

This question is based on a case study and will require details about a specific area of coastline. An excellent example would be Swanage Bay in Dorset.

# Swanage Bay and Durlston Bay

Many coastal regions have to be **protected** from erosion. You will need to refer to a specific case study for this unit.

Swanage Bay and Durlston Bay are in Dorset, on the south coast of England.

**Case study**

You need to know a case study of how a coast is managed.

## Geology

The Dorset coastline is made up of bands of hard, **resistant** rocks and soft, **less resistant** rocks. This type of geology causes **headlands** and **bays** to form.

Soft rocks (Greensand and Wealden Beds) easily eroded by wave action form bays.

Swanage Bay

Swanage

Peveril Point

Durlston Bay

Durlston Head

Hard resistant rocks (Purbeck Beds and Portland Stone) create headlands such as Pervil Point and Durlston Head.

## Coastal management

Swanage Bay and Durlston Bay are protected against erosion by a range of **hard** and **soft** engineering techniques. These solutions are expensive, with £2.2 m spent recently on groynes and beach replenishment.

**Swanage Bay**
Hard:
- sea wall (which is used as a seafront promenade)
- groynes

Soft:
- cliff re-grading
- beach replenishment

**Durlston Bay**
Hard:
- rip rap
- cliff drainage (excess water drained from cliffs to prevent **slumping**)

Soft:
- cliff re-grading

**Worked example** C

Study the photograph. It shows a beach with groynes.

1  Are these groynes an example of hard or soft engineering?  **(1 mark)**

   Hard engineering

2  Groynes such as the ones shown in the photograph protect cliffs from erosion. Explain how.  **(3 marks)**

   Building groynes helps minimise the amount of sand moved along the coastline. They help trap the sand as it moves along the beach by longshore drift, and so it builds up against the up-drift side of the groyne. Longshore drift can help build up beaches, which provide a natural defence against wave energy.

You should mention the link between groynes and **longshore drift** and how this leads to the build-up of beaches.

In your explanation, link the processes together.

Remember that groynes do not cause waves to break!

**Now try this** C

Soft engineering is a way of managing the coastline. Describe the advantages and disadvantages of soft engineering techniques.  **(4 marks)**

Your answer should include advantages **and** disadvantages.

# The Cornish coastline

Cornwall is a county in the south-west of England. The geology of its coastlines is varied but it is mainly granite. This means the coast is resistant to erosion but it is affected by a long fetch and high wave energy. Parts of the coastline are important for recreation, tourism, industry and conservation and are protected by a variety of hard and soft engineering.

**Case study**

You need to know a case study of how a coast is managed.

## Coastal management

### Hard engineering

**Rip rap revetments,** e.g. at Widemouth Bay – absorb wave energy and reduce erosion and landslides.

**Gabions,** e.g. at Port Gwidden – gabions are wire mesh baskets filled with rocks that absorb wave energy.

**Sea walls,** e.g. at Mousehole and Marazion – built to protect harbours which are important for recreation and industry.

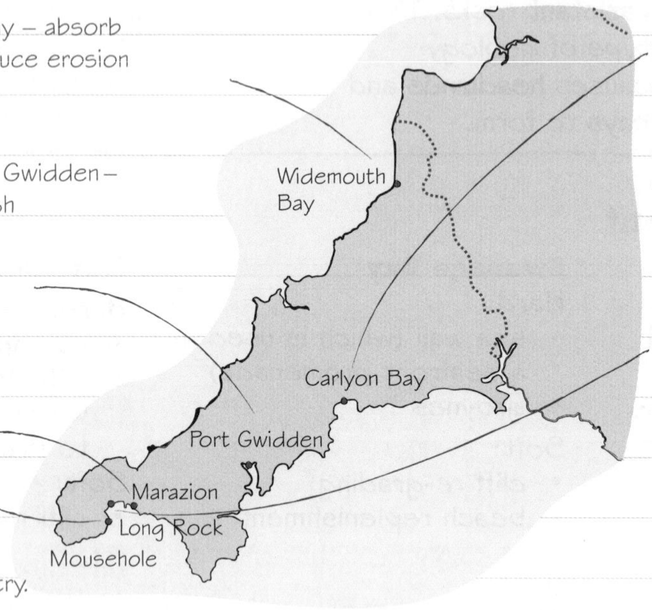

### Soft engineering

**Beach replenishment,** e.g. at Carlyon Bay – used to prevent the loss of coastal footpaths and to create a natural defence against wave energy.

**Dune stabilisation,** e.g. at Long Rock – sand dunes absorb wave energy and reduce erosion of coast. Stabilising them stops the dunes from shifting up the beach where they have less impact.

*Map labels: Widemouth Bay, Carlyon Bay, Port Gwidden, Marazion, Long Rock, Mousehole*

## Worked example

Outline how the length of fetch can affect the rate of coastal erosion.

**(4 marks)**

A large fetch will result in larger and stronger waves. This will therefore have more erosive power and cliff recession will increase.

- Don't confuse fetch with the speed of the wind.
- Make clear whether you are talking about more or less erosion.

## Now try this

Choose an area of coastline you have studied. **Explain** how this area of coastline is being managed.

**(6 marks)**

Remember to refer to a named example in your answer.

# River basins

There are a number of important key terms used when describing river basins. You will need to know these terms and how to use them.

## Key terms

You need to be able to use the correct key terms to label a map, photograph or diagram of a river basin.

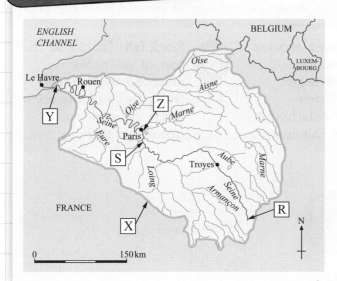

**Source** – the start of the river, often a spring or a lake

**Drainage basin** – the area drained by a river and its tributaries

**Watershed** – the boundary between one drainage basin and another

**Tributary** – a small stream or river that joins a bigger one

**Confluence** – where two rivers meet

**Mouth or Estuary** – where the river meets the sea

## Worked example

FOUND D

1  X is a feature of a drainage basin.
   **Name** feature X.
   ☐ **A** source
   ☐ **B** mouth
   ☐ **C** tributary
   ☒ **D** watershed                    **(1 mark)**

2  **Name** the drainage basin features Y and Z shown on the map.          **(2 marks)**

   Y Source, Z Confluence

For question 1 you need to know **where** the different features of a drainage basin are located.

Make sure you learn the **definition** of each key term, to help you with questions similar to question 2.

## Now try this

What is the difference between the confluence and a tributary?

**(2 marks)**

This is where learning the **meanings** of the different terms will help. Remember you need to **compare** the two terms in this question.

# Processes affecting river valleys

You will need to be able to understand and explain the processes that affect river valleys.

## Erosion

Erosion is the wearing away of the banks and bed of a river. These processes help remove material.

A river can erode **laterally** (widening the channel) or **vertically** (deepening the channel).

## Weathering processes

Weathering is the wearing away of the river valley sides. There are three weathering processes common to river valleys. These take place **in situ** but the weathered material may move due to gravity and form **scree** slopes.

**1** **Physical** (freeze–thaw)

Water freezes and the crack is widened

**2** **Chemical** (acid rain) – rain water is lightly acidic, the acid reacts with minerals in the rocks and dissolves them.

**3** **Biological**

Acids released by vegetation speed up chemical weathering.

Roots grow into cracks and split rocks apart

## Mass movement

Over time the sides of a river valley become less **steep** as material is moved from the top to the bottom. There are three main types of movement:

**1** **Soil creep** – soil **particles** move down the slope under influence of gravity.

**2** **Slumping** – the river erodes the bottom of the valley slope making it steeper. Material above slides downwards, particularly if it is **saturated** with rain water.

**3** **Rock fall** – rocks at the top of valley are affected by freeze–thaw. Parts of the rock break off and move down the slope.

## Worked example

Compare the processes of hydraulic action and attrition. **(4 marks)**

HIGHER B-A

Attrition and hydraulic action are forms of river erosion – they both wear away and remove material from the sides and bed of the river. Hydraulic action is when the river water hits the sides and base of the river and so is very effective when the river water is fast flowing. In comparison, attrition is when river material becomes more rounded and smaller as components smash against each other in the water.

The **command word** in the question makes it clear what is expected.

When **comparing**, make sure you include both the **similarities** and **differences** between your key words. You can use the words 'in comparison' to make it clear you are answering the question.

## Now try this

FOUND D

Mass movement can occur in river valleys. **Explain** the process of mass movement. **(3 marks)**

In this type of question, you do not need to explain all three types of mass movement. You can just explain one of them in detail.

# The long profile

The **profile** of a river changes from the **source** to the **mouth**. You will need to know how and why it changes.

The long profile

---

## Characteristics of a river

The characteristics of a river change from its upper to lower courses.

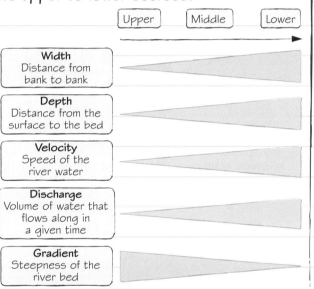

Upper | Middle | Lower

**Width**
Distance from bank to bank

**Depth**
Distance from the surface to the bed

**Velocity**
Speed of the river water

**Discharge**
Volume of water that flows along in a given time

**Gradient**
Steepness of the river bed

## Changes to the river valley

The **vertical** (downwards) and **lateral** (sideways) erosion caused by the river produces distinctive valleys. These can change as the river moves through its course.

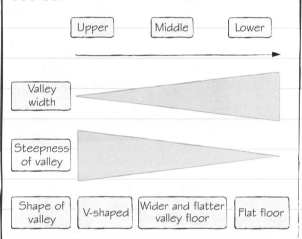

Upper | Middle | Lower

Valley width

Steepness of valley

Shape of valley | V-shaped | Wider and flatter valley floor | Flat floor

---

## Worked example

The characteristics of a river change as it flows along its course. Outline how these characteristics change. **(4 marks)**

The speed of the river will increase. As the velocity increases, the more erosive power the water will have, and so the depth of the channel increases downstream. With increased river speed, more material (load) can be moved, which can further erode the banks of the river, therefore making them much wider further downstream.

You should refer to three different **characteristics** and give some **explanation**. You could also include the characteristics of its valley!

### EXAM ALERT!

Make sure you know the five main characteristics of rivers. Many candidates struggle because they focus on landforms (such as waterfalls and flood plains).

Students have struggled with exam questions similar to this – **be prepared!** ResultsPlus

---

## Now try this

**Explain** why the discharge of a river increases between its **source** and **mouth**. **(4 marks)**

# Upper river landforms

You need to know how and why distinctive landforms develop in the upper course of a river.

In the upper course, the river erodes **vertically** (downwards). At this point the **gradient** is steep and the **channel** is narrow.

## Landforms

### Interlocking spurs

The river at its source is small and has limited energy. It flows naturally from side to side, around ridges in the valley sides, called spurs. The spurs become interlocking with those on the other side of the valley.

### Waterfalls

Waterfalls are a common feature in the upper course of a river, where there is an increase in vertical erosion. They form where there is a layer of hard, resistant rock (the cap rock) overlying a softer, less resistant rock.

Interlocking spurs

River channel

Hard, resistant rock

Waterfall retreats upstream, leaving a steep-sided **gorge**

Overhang gradually collapses

Undercutting

Soft, less resistant rock, eroded by **hydraulic action** (when water is forced into cracks)

**Plunge pool** formed by hydraulic action and **abrasion** (rocks wearing away the bed)

---

## Worked example

**FOUNDN E**

Look at the cross-sectional diagram. It shows how a river landform changed between 1900 and 2000.

1900

2000

Harder rock (limestone)

Softer rock (sandstone)

Y

X   Y

Harder rock (limestone)

Softer rock (sandstone)

0  10  20  30  40  50 metres

**1** Which landform is shown?          **(1 mark)**

☐ **A** meander          ☐ **C** interlocking spur

☐ **B** embankment       ☒ **D** waterfall

**2** How much has the hard rock moved back between **Y** and **X**?     **(1 mark)**

☐ **A** 10m          ☒ **C** 25m

☐ **B** 50m          ☐ **D** 40m

Look at the diagram carefully. Take note of any extra detail such as the **scale**.

You will need a ruler to help you answer questions like this.

---

## Now try this

**HIGHER B-A**

**Explain** how a waterfall is formed. Use an **annotated** diagram or diagrams in your answer.     **(4 marks)**

Your diagram should include **explanatory** notes about the formation of a waterfall rather than just **describing** the landform.

# Middle river landforms 1

The characteristics of the middle course of the river produce distinctive landforms – **meanders**, **slip-off slopes** and **river cliffs**. You need to know how these landforms develop.

## Meanders

In the middle course, the **width**, **depth** and **velocity** of the river all increase. The river erodes **laterally** (sideways) and so starts to form large bends. The bends get bigger and wider, and eventually develop into a horseshoe shape called a **meander**.

See also p. 29

For more on width, depth and velocity.

On the outer bend of a meander, where the current is faster, there is greater **erosion**. This wears away the bank creating a **river cliff**.

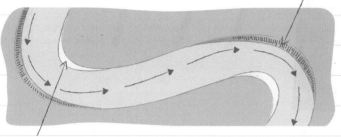

River cliff

Slip-off slope

On the inner bend of a meander where the current is slower, there is greater **deposition**, creating a slip-off slope.

## Worked example

**HIGHER A**

**Explain** the **formation** of a **meander**.
You may use a diagram in your answer.          **(4 marks)**

Meanders form through erosion processes such as hydraulic action and abrasion. This tends to occur on the outside bend of the meander so undercuts the river bank – this then forms a steep slope called a river cliff.

The cliff continues to be eroded and eventually collapses. The inside bend has the slowest flow and the river is forced to deposit its load as the energy is too low to keep sediment in suspension. This moves the bend forward towards the outside bend. The process repeats and the meanders get bigger in size.

Remember that a meander has two sides – an outer and inner bend. To do well you need to **explain** the processes on both sides.

If you use a diagram make sure it is **annotated**!

## Now try this

**FOUNDN D**

Look at the sketch showing a **meander** bend.

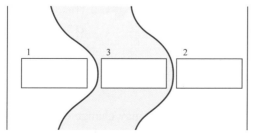

Label boxes 1 and 2 with the correct terms **river cliff** and **slip-off slope**. **Draw** an arrow in the correct place in box 3 to show the fastest flow of the river.          **(3 marks)**

# Middle river landforms 2

Another distinctive middle river landform is the **oxbow lake**. You need to know how this landform develops.

## Formation of oxbow lakes

An oxbow lake forms as part of a bend in the river meander, and occurs when a meander is cut off from the main river. Over time, oxbow lakes may dry up. Meanders and oxbow lakes are more evident in the lower course of a river.

An oxbow lake

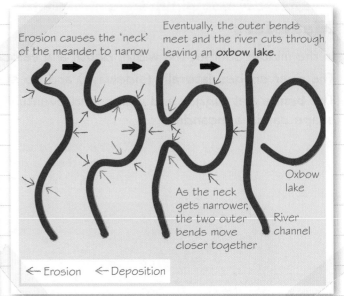

Erosion causes the 'neck' of the meander to narrow

Eventually, the outer bends meet and the river cuts through leaving an **oxbow lake**.

As the neck gets narrower, the two outer bends move closer together

Oxbow lake

River channel

← Erosion    ← Deposition

---

## Worked example

HIGHER **A**

Describe the formation of an oxbow lake.  **(4 marks)**

Rivers can erode laterally (side to side). Erosion is greatest on the outside of the meander bend and forces the neck of the meander to narrow. At the same time, on the inside bend, deposition occurs. Over time, this will make the meander loop wider and the neck narrower. Eventually, the neck of the meander bends will join together and the meander is removed from the river current creating a crescent shaped feature called an oxbow lake.

With any formation questions, make sure your answer is in a logical sequence. Think about describing the formation as it happens **over time**. Make sure you don't miss out any stages or repeat yourself.

Include an annotated diagram to help support your answer.

---

## Now try this

HIGHER **C**

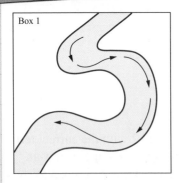

Box 1

Box 2

Think about how the **shape** of the meander will change and develop over time.

Look at the diagram of a meander in Box 1.

In Box 2, draw a labelled diagram to show how the meander may change over time.    **(3 marks)**

# Lower river landforms

The characteristics of the lower course of the river produce distinctive landforms – **flood plains** and **levees**. You need to know how and why these landforms develop.

## Flood plains

A flood plain is the wide, flat area of land either side of a river and experiences floods when the river tops its banks.

> In the lower course, the river is nearing the sea and carries a huge amount of sediment (**alluvium**).

> When the river floods, excess water spills over the surrounding area.

> During flooding, the **velocity** of the river is reduced, it loses energy, and deposits sediment, forming the flood plain.

> The flood plain is shaped by the **lateral** erosion of meanders as they gradually migrate downstream and by deposition of material on the inner bends.

## How levees develop

The deposition process, which takes place during flooding, continues until eventually embankments are created beside the river. These are called **levees**.

Before a flood

During a flood — When flooding occurs, the heaviest material is deposited first due to the decrease in the river's energy. This material creates natural embankments called levees.

After a flood — The smaller and finer sediment, or alluvium, is deposited further from the river because it requires less energy to carry it.

---

## Worked example

Describe the formation of levees.
Use a diagram in your answer.　　**(4 marks)**

When a river floods, the sediment is deposited on the flood plain adjoining the river. This is the start of the formation of a levee or embankment. The heavier material is dropped near the river channel due to the loss of energy. After a number of flood events, further alluvium is deposited on top and this builds up to form levees.

 1　 2　Flood　 3 Lighter Heavier material material　 4

When drawing formation diagrams, remember to:
- draw them in sequence
- number them to show the correct order
- annotate them!

---

## Now try this

Study the cross-sectional diagram. It shows river landforms.

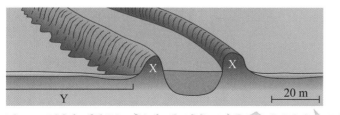

1　Name landforms X and Y.　　**(2 marks)**
2　Describe landforms X and Y.　　**(3 marks)**

You need to give **three** points about the two landforms. You can include data from the scale.

# Why do rivers flood?

Flooding has a combination of **physical** and **human** causes. You will need to know these causes, and why they happen.

## Physical causes of flooding

| Rainfall intensity | Geology | Snow melt | Drainage basin |
|---|---|---|---|
| A lot of rainfall over a short period of time prevents soil **infiltration**. | Rocks like granite are **impermeable**, so water is unable to **percolate** from the thin soil above. | At spring time warmer temperatures will **melt** snow creating more water. | Steep-sided valleys or a lot of **tributaries** means the water enters the river system quicker. |

Excess water will flow towards the river as **surface run-off (overland flow)** or **groundwater**.

Water will reach the river channel more quickly and forces level of river to rise above bank full. Flooding can then occur.

## Human causes of flooding

| Deforestation | Climate change | Urbanisation |
|---|---|---|
| Once vegetation has been cleared, this decreases **interception storage**. | **Melting** of ice sheets and glaciers as global temperatures increase. More water will flow into rivers. | Rain is forced to flow rapidly into sewers and drains as man-made surfaces are impermeable. |

Excess water will flow towards the river as **surface run-off (overland flow)** or **groundwater flow**.

Water reaches the river channel more quickly and forces level of river to rise above bank full. Flooding can then occur.

## Worked example

**HIGHER B**

Explain **one** human and **one** physical cause of flooding. **(4 marks)**

The command word is **explain** so you must make reference to the **processes** involved.

A human cause is deforestation. Cutting down trees means there is less interception and absorption of rain. This means the rain water quickly enters the river which could result in flooding.

A physical cause is saturated ground from previously wet weather. When the ground cannot absorb any more water, any excess is forced to flow over the ground as surface run-off, and therefore it enters river channels much more quickly, which could lead to flooding.

### EXAM ALERT!

For each cause you mention, try to write about different consequences, e.g. in this student answer, they have talked about surface run-off for each of their causes.

Students have struggled with exam questions similar to this – **be prepared!**  ResultsPlus

## Now try this

Afforestation is a type of soft engineering.
State **one** advantage and **one** disadvantage of afforestation.

**(2 marks)**

# River Stour, Dorset

The River Stour has been experiencing floods since 1756. This has had major **impacts** on the small town of Blandford Forum. You will need to know the **causes** of these floods and about the attempts to **manage** the river.

**Case study**

You need to know a case study of the management of a riverine area.

## River Stour flooding, 1979

### Physical causes
- Impermeable clay layer
- Dense network of streams
- Narrow flood plain
- Heavy rainfall

### Human causes
- Land use change from woodland to farming

### Effects

Social and Economic effects

- Damage to property (140 properties damaged)

- Flooding of streets made transport of goods and people difficult
- Hotels and shops flooded – increased insurance claims
- Farmland flooded and crops destroyed

Environmental effects

- Wildlife affected, e.g. the nests of ground-nesting birds may be washed away along with their eggs

## Management strategies

The River Stour has been managed through a combination of **hard** and **soft** engineering. In 1986 a flood management scheme was set up to protect Blandford. The scheme has cost £1.45 million, but is estimated to have saved £1.6 million in flood damage. The scheme is therefore reducing the **economic impact**.

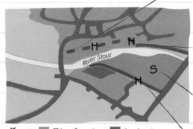

Key: ■ Blanford ■ Industry
H Hard engineering
S Soft engineering

**Flood wall** 2.5 m high with a relief channel 1m deep behind it. This protects houses and shops in the town centre.

**Pumping station** pumps excess water downstream to help prevent flooding.

**Washlands** allow excess water to spread out.

**Flood bank** creates a barrier which protects the brewery, industrial estate and houses.

## Worked example

**Explain** how flooding can be caused by **physical** factors.

**(4 marks)**

Clay is an impermeable layer, found for example in the upper course of the River Stour. Water cannot infiltrate through this layer and is forced to flow over the surface. The water will reach the river very quickly. In flood events, heavy rainfall (5 cm in 24 h.) can lead to flooding, as there is rapid surface run-off into the river because the volume of rainfall makes it impossible to infiltrate into the soil.

Make sure you use correct **terminology** and, as the question asks refer only to **physical** factors.

## Now try this

**Explain** the effects of flooding on people and the environment. Use examples in your answer. **(6 marks)**

Make sure you include **examples** in your answer, giving the name and context.

# Mississippi, USA (2011)

The Mississippi flooded in April and May 2011. You will need to know why the river floods and how this is being managed.

**Case study**

You need to know a case study of the management of a riverine area.

## Mississippi flooding, 2011

### Physical causes

- Heavy rainfall and snowfall – rainfall in Kentucky four times the normal amount
- High proportion of tornadoes

### Human causes

- Increased development of impermeable surfaces on flood plains

### Impacts

Social

Outbreak of disease, e.g. tetanus and E. coli, loss of life

Social and Economic

Homes flooded
Cost of insurance, fuel and food increases

Economic and Environmental

Fertilisers needed to replace nutrients washed away, crops and farmland destroyed

Remember, you may need to comment on the impacts of flooding using a range of examples.

## Management strategies

### Hard engineering

**1** Levees built since eighteenth century

**2** River straightening

**3** **Floodways** and **cut offs** divert water in times of flood

### Soft engineering

**1** Subsidised insurance scheme to regulate land use on the floodplain

**2** Agricultural land that has been flooded purchased to store excess water

**3** Restoration of upriver wetland areas to act as sponges during heavy rainfall

**4** Government funding for farmers who convert land into wildlife conservation reserves and water storage areas

---

**Worked example**

 FOUND'N D–C

Choose a river that you have studied. Outline **one** way in which the river has been managed. **(2 marks)**

The Mississippi: Since the 1700s, hard engineering techniques such as levees have been used. These were built to raise the height of the channel and increase the channel capacity, allowing the river to carry more water, and stop it spilling onto the land.

The command word in the question is **outline**. You need to give details of the techniques used, rather than just describe them.

**Now try this**

 HIGHER C

Suggest how soft engineering methods can reduce the effects of flooding. **(4 marks)**

Remember to refer to more than **one** soft engineering technique.

# Reducing the impact of flooding

There are strategies that can help reduce the impact of flooding on people and the environment. Make sure you know examples of these strategies, and how they work.

## Planning

Areas at risk from flooding are used for parks and leisure activities, to reduce the impact of flooding. This is called **land use zoning**, e.g. Nome, Alaska.

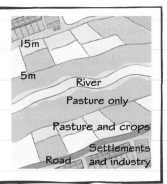

15m
5m
River
Pasture only
Pasture and crops
Settlements and industry
Road

After the flooding of Boscastle in 2004, the EA built new overflow channels to carry excess water.

## Prediction

It is difficult to predict exactly when a flood event will occur. Organisations such as the UK Environment Agency (EA) and the US Federal Emergency Management Agency (FEMA) **monitor** rivers. They use this information to:

- help forecast potential flood events
- give advance warning of flooding.

## Prevention

The EA gives advice on how to reduce flood damage to homes, for example:
- use ceramic tiles instead of carpet
- raise the height of electrical sockets on walls
- use synthetic materials for windows and doors
- install heating systems on upper floors.

In many Low Income Countries (LICs) homes are often built on stilts to raise them above the flood risk level.

## Education

The EA helps reduce the **impact** of flooding by keeping people up to date with strategies and emergency plans. Its methods include:
- leaflets and advertising
- posting information on its website
- telephone helplines
- organising flood drills.

Flood drills are common in schools along the Missouri River (Nebraska) and Green River (Washington) in the USA.

## Worked example

HIGHER C

Outline how river flooding can be reduced through planning and prevention. **(3 marks)**

Planning – You could have an action plan which could give warnings to people so that they can move away. Households could also use sandbags.

Building design – All electricity sockets could be higher up on the wall, so that flood water cannot reach them.

Use this mnemonic to help you remember:

<u>P</u>enelope ......... P for Planning
<u>P</u>refers ............ P for Prediction
<u>P</u>ink ................. P for Prevention
<u>E</u>lephants ....... E for Education

## Now try this

Describe how the effects of river flooding can be reduced through prediction and prevention. Use examples in your answer. **(4 marks)**

# Flood management: soft engineering

You need to make sure you know examples of soft engineering, and how they help prevent river flooding. Soft engineering is often considered more **environmentally friendly**.

**Afforestation** – replanting trees within the drainage basin

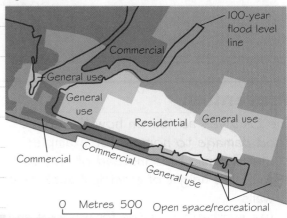

👍 Vegetation soaks up and **intercepts** water, so less reaches the river channel.

👍 Woodlands provide wildlife habitats and reduce **visual pollution**.

👎 The opportunity to use land for other purposes is reduced.

## Land use zoning

👍 Expensive projects and residential can be located in low risk areas.

👍 Leisure and recreation can be located in high risk areas.

**See also p. 37**
For more land use zoning.

👎 Access for the public may be more difficult.

👎 May cause planning problems elsewhere in the region.

**Washlands** – areas on the floodplain which are allowed to flood

👍 A relatively cheap way to solve the problem of excess flood water.

👍 Less visual pollution.

👎 Use of the floodplain for other purposes is restricted, e.g. industry and agriculture.

Many rivers will use a combination of hard and soft engineering techniques. For example, the Rhine, Mississippi and the Stour.

## Worked example

Suggest how soft engineering methods can reduce the effects of flooding. **(4 marks)**

Soft engineering processes work with the river to reduce effects of flooding. For instance, afforestation (planting vegetation) means that roots and leaves can intercept rain water, and reduces the amount of water getting into the river. Flood plain zoning prohibits buildings from being erected, leaving the soil free to soak up rain water and increasing the time it takes for run-off to occur. This then reduces the water volume that reaches the river. Warning systems alert people living nearby and allow them time to prepare.

Try to explain at least **two** types of soft engineering and be sure to **describe** how they reduce flooding rather than just state what they are.

## Now try this

Soft engineering is a way of managing river flooding. Describe the advantages and disadvantages of soft engineering techniques. **(4 marks)**

You need to describe both the advantages and disadvantages to gain full marks.

# Flood management: hard engineering

Hard engineering techniques offer more radical solutions for the prevention of river flooding. You will need to know examples of hard engineering, and how they help prevent rivers from flooding.

 **Flood relief channels** – extra channels to carry surplus water
- ✓ Surplus water is channelled from the river, preventing it from flooding nearby land.
- ✗ Visually unattractive.
- ✗ Only needed when there is a flood risk.
- ✗ Expensive to build and maintain.

 **Channelisation** – deepening or widening of the river channel
- ✓ Allows water to flow more quickly, away from areas of flood risk.
- ✗ Visually unattractive.
- ✗ More water is taken **downstream**, increasing the flood risk to other settlements.

 **Embankments** – levees built on or near the river banks
- ✓ Use **natural** materials which blend in with the surrounding landscape.
- ✓ Prevent water moving into areas at risk.
- ✗ Flood water can spill over in extreme conditions.
- ✗ Can burst under pressure which can cause widespread damage.

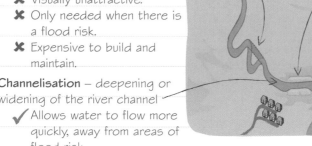

## Worked example

Study the photograph.
It shows a river in Los Angeles, USA.

1 Is the flood management shown in the photograph an example of hard or soft engineering?

**(1 mark)**

Hard engineering

2 Explain how the flood management shown in the photograph could help to reduce erosion.

**(3 marks)**

The embankments are made of concrete which provides a resistant surface; therefore the rate of erosion is slower. The banks are much smoother allowing higher velocity and reducing erosion as there is less friction.

You need to give a clear explanation of how the use of concrete helps reduce erosion.

## Now try this

Embankments (levees) are an example of hard engineering.
State **one** advantage and **one** disadvantage of embankments.

**(2 marks)**

# Earthquakes and volcanoes

Earthquakes and volcanoes occur in different parts of the world. You need to be able to explain why and where they occur, and know an example of each.

## What's the pattern?

**Earthquakes** and **volcanoes** are found in many different parts of the world. The two are often found in the same places. They tend to occur in narrow bands, that are found:

- in the middle of oceans, such as the Atlantic
- along the edges of continents, such as the west coast of America.

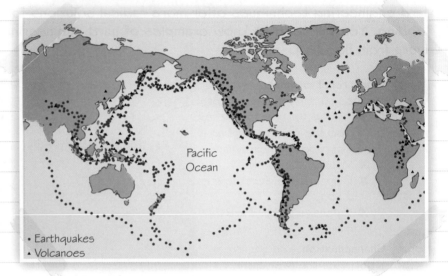

Pacific Ocean

• Earthquakes
▲ Volcanoes

---

**Worked example**

Describe the **distribution** of volcanoes shown on the map below. Use **evidence** from the map in your answer.

**(4 marks)**

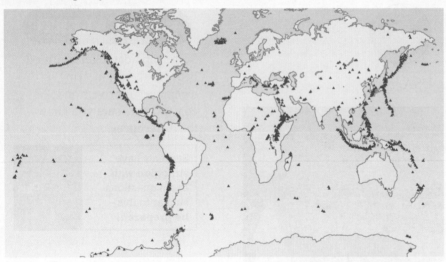

The question asks you to use specific **evidence** from the map. This can include data or detail about places (for example, the Pacific Ocean).

The volcanoes are in lines along coasts or clustered together along plate boundaries, such as Mount Etna on the destructive plate boundary of the Eurasian plate and the African plate. Some are found in the centre of the ocean. These are called hotspots and an example is Hawaii in the middle of the Pacific plate. There is a particularly high number of volcanoes along the edges of the Pacific Ocean.

---

**Now try this**

Describe the **distribution** of earthquakes and volcanoes on a global scale.

**(4 marks)**

Try to make three different points.

40

# Plate tectonics

Volcanoes and earthquakes occur in similar places – this is due to **plate tectonics**.

## Tectonic plates

The Earth's **crust** is divided into giant sections called **tectonic plates**.

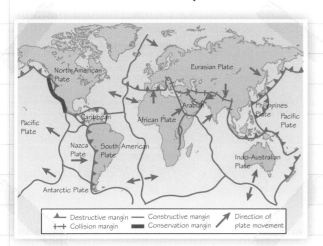

Tectonic plates are made up of two types of **crust**.

| Oceanic crust | Continental crust |
|---|---|
| Consists of younger rocks | Older rocks |
| Heavier or denser | Lighter or less dense |
| Thinner: <10 km thick | Thicker: 25–70 km thick |

## Plate movement

Tectonic plates move as a result of **convection currents** in the Earth's **mantle**. The type of crust and the movement and direction of plates determine the type of plate boundary and the tectonic activity that occurs there.

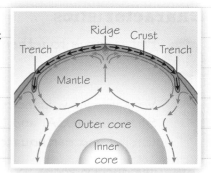

There are three types of plate boundary: **convergent**, **divergent** and **conservative**.

**See also pp. 42, 43 and 44**

For more on types of plate boundary.

Volcanoes and earthquakes tend to occur at plate boundaries but some volcanoes occur in the middle of tectonic plates where the crust is thin and hot magma can escape. These are called **hotspots**. If this occurs under the sea, the lava can build up to form islands, e.g. Hawaii and Lanzarote.

## Worked example

Look at the map of tectonic plates.

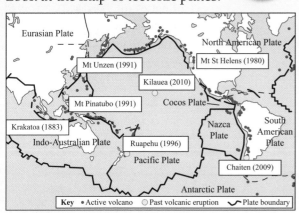

The volcano Kilauea is formed on a:

☐ **A** convergent plate boundary
☒ **B** hotspot
☐ **C** conservative plate boundary
☐ **D** divergent plate boundary **(1 mark)**

Make sure that you look at the resource indicated by the question, and locate the correct volcano.

## Now try this

The island of Lanzarote off the Atlantic coast of North Africa has formed over a hotspot.

Explain how volcanoes form over hotspots.

Use an annotated diagram or diagrams in your answer. **(4 marks)**

Remember that **annotations** are **explanatory** notes, not just labels.

# Convergent plate boundaries

**Convergent** (or **destructive**) boundaries are where plates collide. You need to know the characteristic features, and the tectonic activity that occurs at this type of boundary.

## Characteristics

 Plates move together and **collide**.

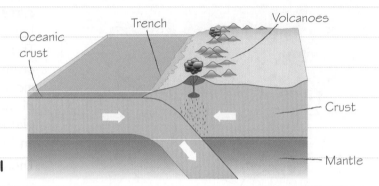

 Very violent **volcanoes** (e.g. Mt St Helens (USA) and Mt Etna (Sicily) and **earthquakes occur**.

**3** **Subduction zones** form due to downward movement of the dense **oceanic** crust into the **mantle**, beneath the less dense **continental** crust.

**4** **Fold mountains** (e.g. the Alps and the Himalayas) can form when both plates are pushed upwards by the force of the collision.

---

## Worked example

**C** HIGHER

Study the diagram of a plate boundary.

1  What type of plate boundary is shown? **(1 mark)**
Convergent (destructive)

2  Draw arrows on the diagram to show the direction of the plate movement. **(1 mark)**

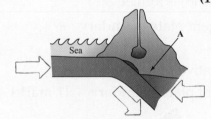

3  Name the type of plate shown at A. **(1 mark)**
Continental

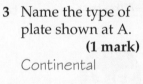

Make sure you can identify different types of plate margins from diagrams. You may be required to label them.

When showing **plate direction** on a diagram, always include **two** arrows to indicate which way **both** plates are moving.

---

## Now try this

**C** HIGHER

State two characteristics of a **convergent** plate boundary.

**(2 marks)**

Learn three or four **features** of each plate boundary. Remember that some features occur at more than one type of boundary.

# Divergent plate boundaries

**Divergent** (or **constructive**) boundaries are where plates move apart. You need to know the characteristics of this boundary type.

## Characteristics

**1** Plates move **apart**.

**2** Less violent **volcanoes** and **earthquakes occur**.

**3** New **sea floor** is created at mid-ocean **ridges** (e.g. the Mid-Atlantic Ridge) as **magma** rises up through the ridge and solidifies.

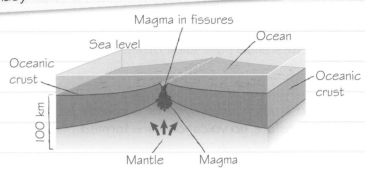

Examples of volcanoes at divergent boundaries: Mt Heimaey and Mt Laki in Iceland

Magma in fissures
Sea level
Ocean
Oceanic crust
Oceanic crust
100 km
Mantle
Magma

## Worked example

HIGHER **B**

Look at the map. It shows rates of plate movement along the Mid-Atlantic Ridge, a divergent plate boundary.

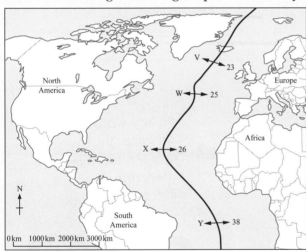

North America
V → 23
Europe
W ← → 25
Africa
X ← → 26
N
South America
Y ← → 38
0 km 1000 km 2000 km 3000 km

X ← → 26 = movement in mm per year, at that point on the plate boundary

The movement along the Mid-Atlantic Ridge plate boundary at point V is diverging at 23 mm per year. At point W this increases to 25 mm per year. At point X (further south) it is moving 26 mm apart each year and finally at point Y it moves apart the most, with 38 mm per year. All four points are diverging along this constructive plate margin.

Always use evidence or data from the map in support of your description.

**1** Which point on the Mid-Atlantic Ridge has the most movement per year? **(1 mark)**

☐ **A** V        ☐ **C** X
☐ **B** W        ☒ **D** Y

**2** Describe the movements shown along this plate boundary. **(3 marks)**

## Now try this

HIGHER **B**

Explain how volcanoes occur at divergent plate boundaries. **(4 marks)**

Pay attention to the command word in this question. Make sure you **explain** the processes involved, rather than just describing them.

Had a look ☐  Nearly there ☐  Nailed it! ☐

# Conservative (transform) plate boundaries

**Conservative** boundaries are where two plates slide past each other. You need to know the characteristics of this boundary type.

## Characteristics

 Plates **slide** past each other.

 No crust is destroyed or created, therefore **no volcanoes** are formed.

 Plates can 'stick'; this increases pressure which can be released as violent **earthquakes**.

An example of a conservative plate boundary is the San Andreas Fault, California, USA

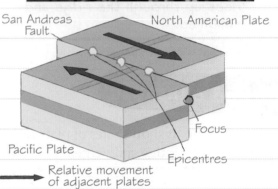

San Andreas Fault · North American Plate · Focus · Pacific Plate · Epicentres · Relative movement of adjacent plates

---

## Worked example

Compare the characteristic features of convergent plate boundaries and conservative plate boundaries. **(4 marks)**

Convergent plate margins are where two plates (any kind) move towards each other. When they meet, the oceanic crust subducts below the continental crust because it is denser. The melted magma rises up under pressure through the continental crust. This movement can cause earthquakes and volcanoes, e.g. Chances Peak.

In comparison, conservative plate margins are where two plates slide past each other, e.g. San Andreas Fault. No volcanoes form here as no crust is being destroyed, but they can create violent earthquakes.

The key word here is **compare**. You should compare the **similarities** or **differences** between the different plate boundaries.

### EXAM ALERT!

Many candidates confuse **conservative** with **divergent** plate boundaries. Make sure you know the difference!

Students have struggled with exam questions similar to this – **be prepared!**

ResultsPlus

---

## Now try this

Explain why volcanoes do not form on conservative plate margins. **(3 marks)**

# Measuring earthquakes

There are two different scales used to measure the **magnitude** (strength) of an earthquake. You need to know the differences between these scales.

## The Richter scale

- It measures the **energy** released during an earthquake.
- The **magnitude** increases 10 fold as you move up the scale because it is a **logarithmic** scale.
- There is no upper limit to the scale.
- A sensitive scientific instrument called a **seismometer** is used.

## The Mercalli scale

- It measures the **effects** or **impacts** of the earthquake, the **damage** done and what people feel (the amount of movement).
- The scale is measured in Roman numerals from I to XII.

## Energy from earthquakes

The energy produced by earthquakes is at its greatest at two key points:

 **Epicentre** – the point on the surface directly **above** the **focus**.

 **Focus** – the central point of the earthquake deep under the surface, where the earthquake actually happens!

Make sure you understand the key terms: **epicentre** and **focus**.
Remember: E comes before F in the alphabet, so E on **top** of land and F **below** ground!

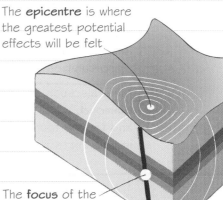

The **epicentre** is where the greatest potential effects will be felt

The **focus** of the earthquake is where there is the greatest release of energy

Fault

## Worked example

HIGHER C-B

Outline the differences between the Mercalli and Richter scales.    **(3 marks)**

The Richter scale measures the magnitude of the earthquake whereas the Mercalli scale measures the damage caused by the quake. The Richter scale has no upper limit whereas the Mercalli scale goes from I to XII.

Pay attention to the command words in this question – make sure you mention more than one difference.
Avoid giving an **opposite** difference. For example, the Richter scale has no upper limit whereas the Mercalli does.

## Now try this

FOUNDN D

How does the epicentre of an earthquake differ from the focus?                    **(2 marks)**

Learning the **definitions** of each key word will help with this type of question!

# Living with hazards

Many people live in areas that are at risk of earthquakes and volcanic eruptions. You need to know the **reasons** why people choose to live in these places.

These reasons can be **social** (people), **environmental** (natural) and **economic** (jobs and income).

|  | Volcanoes | Example | Earthquakes | Example |
|---|---|---|---|---|
| Social | Some people worship earthquakes, believing they are ancient spirits | Mt Merapi, Indonesia (MIC) Mt Fuji, Japan (HIC) | Earthquake-proofed buildings and disaster plans make people feel safer | San Francisco, California, USA (HIC) Japan (HIC) Haiti (LIC) |
| Environmental | Area may attract tourists, bringing jobs and higher income | Mt Etna, Sicily (HIC) Mt Laki or Heimaey, Iceland (HIC) | Often areas of great natural beauty, where people like to live | San Francisco, California, USA (HIC) |
| Economic | Soils are often very fertile, with lots of farming opportunities | The volcanic soils of Colombia are used for coffee crops (MIC) | Some areas offer employment opportunities, with high-income jobs | Silicon Valley, California, USA (HIC) Japan (HIC) |
|  | Minerals such as diamond, gold and tin are found in volcanic soils | Copper, gold and silver mining on Mt St Helens, USA (HIC) | Popular tourist areas and desirable locations, with jobs and income opportunities | Los Angeles, California, USA (HIC) |

## Worked example

Outline **two** reasons why people continue to live in areas affected by volcanic eruptions.     **(4 marks)**

1  Ash from the volcano causes soil to be fertile. This could attract farming and can provide economic benefits such as jobs and income.

2  Many volcanic regions are monitored using tiltmeters and seismometers and so people believe that technology will provide adequate warning.

Do not just list your reasons, but develop each statement to explain why it would encourage people to live in these areas.

## EXAM ALERT!

Many candidates confuse the question and write about **earthquake** areas instead of areas affected by volcanic eruptions.

Students have struggled with exam questions similar to this – **be prepared!**     ResultsPlus

## Now try this

Suggest reasons why people continue to live in areas affected by earthquakes.     **(4 marks)**

Remember to read the question carefully and underline the **command** words. This question focuses on earthquakes and **not** volcanoes.

46

# Chances Peak volcano

Chances Peak is a volcano in the Soufrière Hills, in the southern part of the island of Montserrat, in the Caribbean. It became **active** in 1995 and finally erupted on 25 June 1997. This is a good example for a case study, so make sure you know the causes and impacts of this eruption.

## Causes

Labels 1–4 on the diagram show the sequence of events that caused the Chances Peak eruption.

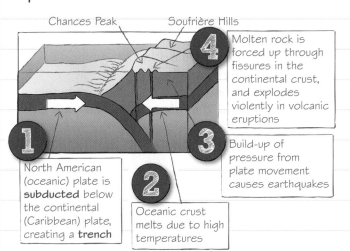

Chances Peak    Soufrière Hills

**4** Molten rock is forced up through fissures in the continental crust, and explodes violently in volcanic eruptions

**3** Build-up of pressure from plate movement causes earthquakes

**1** North American (oceanic) plate is **subducted** below the continental (Caribbean) plate, creating a **trench**

**2** Oceanic crust melts due to high temperatures

## Effects and responses

Effects of the eruption:
- 5 million m³ of ash and rock **deposited**
- Trants village covered in 4 km² of ash
- 19 people killed.
- 100–150 homes destroyed
- Bramble airport destroyed, disrupting air traffic
- people's feet and car tyres burnt by ash.

Responses to the eruption:
- The Montserrat Volcano Observatory was set up to **monitor** seismic activity.
- **Face masks** were issued to children to prevent silicosis.
- 7000 people were **evacuated** from the island and the immediate danger zone.

## Worked example

**FOUNDⁿ D**

Sea    A

1  What **type** of plate boundary is shown? **(1 mark)**
Convergent

2  Name the **type** of plate shown at **A** on the diagram. **(1 mark)**
Continental

**EXAM ALERT!**

Remember to use the correct terminology from the exam specification. Many candidates have used destructive rather than convergent to describe this plate boundary. This is not incorrect but **convergent** is the term used in the specification.

Students have struggled with exam questions similar to this – **be prepared!**    ResultsPlus

## Now try this

**HIGHER A-A***

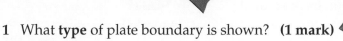

Choose a volcanic eruption you have studied. Explain the effects of the eruption on people and the environment.    **(6 marks)**

You must **explain** the effects and not just list them! Make separate lists of impacts on people and the environment – this may help you to write it up.

# Bam earthquake (2003)

At 5.26am on 26 December 2003, an earthquake measuring an estimated 6.5 on the Richter scale hit the city of Bam in Iran.

**Case study**

You need to know a case study of the causes and effects of an earthquake or volcanic eruption.

## Causes

The earthquake occurred due to a build-up of **pressure** generated by the **collision** of the Arabian plate moving northwards against the Eurasian plate (a **convergent plate margin**).

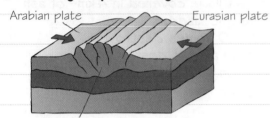

Arabian plate    Eurasian plate

Fold mountains form and earthquakes occur due to pressure building up from the collision of the plates, which move at 3 cm per year

## Effects

The effects of the earthquake were devastating:

Social
- 30000 people killed and 50000 injured
- 100000 homeless
- two hospitals collapsed
- power and communication lines damaged.

Environmental
- fissures or faults formed in the ground
- landslides and rock falls
- collapse of ground under irrigation channels
- loss of palm and date trees due to lack of irrigation.

The impacts were huge because most people were in bed at the time of the earthquake.

## Short-term response
- 92000 tents and 200000 blankets distributed to keep the homeless warm.
- 56000 items of clothing and 51000 oil heaters supplied.
- 400000 ready meals provided.
- 250 emergency hospital beds set up by Iranian Red Crescent, supported by Red Cross.

## Long-term response
- Plans to rebuild the city – 6 months taken to draft a plan.
- Earthquake-proof housing now being built.

There was anger from local people when aid didn't arrive quickly enough. Fresh drinking water wasn't available until 4 weeks after the event.

## Worked example

Choose a volcanic eruption **or** an earthquake you have studied. Describe the causes of the volcanic eruption **or** earthquake.  **(4 marks)**

On 26 December 2003, a 6.5 earthquake hit Bam in Iran. The earthquake was caused by two plates moving into each other. This is called a convergent plate margin. The Arabian plate is moving into the Eurasian. They move at about 3 cm / yr. As they hit each other, mountains form. At the meeting point, earthquakes occur due to the stress caused by the plates moving.

Make sure you know the **differences** between the **causes** of the tectonic hazard and the **effects**.

## Now try this

Choose an earthquake you have studied. Explain the effects of the earthquake on the people and the environment.  **(6 marks)**

# Preventing tectonic hazards

**Planning** can help reduce the impact of volcanic eruptions and volcanoes. You need to know how this can be done, and give examples of the methods used.

## Planning and prevention

We cannot stop tectonic hazards from happening, but there are ways to reduce the impact of volcanic eruptions and earthquakes:

**Volcanic eruptions**

- **Barriers or ditches** – made from concrete or rock are used to **divert** lava flow away from settlements (e.g. Mt Etna, 1991–93)

- **Water spraying** – is used to cool down and **solidify** lava flow (e.g. Mt Heimaey, Iceland, 1973)

- **Land use planning** – ensures that buildings are not built too high or close to a volcano

- **The Emergency services** – need to be **equipped** and **trained** to deal with hazards effectively

- **Education** – makes sure that people know what to do when a hazard occurs (e.g. Disaster Day in Japan is 1 September)

**Earthquakes**

- **Earthquake-proof buildings** – using cross bracing, counter-weights, ball bearings and rubber foundations help **stabilise** buildings (e.g. the triangular design of the Transamerica Pyramid, San Francisco. Its wide, stable base and steel frame allows the building to sway)

## Worked example

Suggest reasons why many of the buildings in the picture did not fall down. **(3 marks)**

Kobe is in Japan, which is a HIC and so can afford to **earthquake-proof** its buildings by using **cross bracing** or **rubber foundations**. This means that the buildings are made to withstand an earthquake and less likely to collapse.

This photo shows an area of Kobe affected by an earthquake.

You may come across several types of photographs in geography (see page 1).

Make sure you look at a photograph carefully to answer the question.

## Now try this

Explain how the effects of volcanic eruptions are reduced through prevention. **(4 marks)**

Candidates often confuse **prediction** and **prevention**. Make sure you know the differences between them and have examples of each.

Had a look ☐  Nearly there ☐  Nailed it! ☐

# Predicting tectonic hazards

Predicting volcanic eruptions and earthquakes can help reduce their impact. You need to know examples of how this is done.

## Prediction instruments

Several **instruments** are used to monitor seismic activity to help **predict** when tectonic hazards may occur:

**1** **Tiltmeters** and **lasers** – measure the change in the **slope** of the land (for example, the San Andreas Fault, California).

**2** **Seismometers** – measure the **seismic waves** produced from an earthquakes (for example, Chances Peak, 1997).

**3** **GPS** and **satellite images** – monitor the **bulging** (shape) of volcanoes and changes in ground heat (for example, Mt St Helens, 1980).

**4** **Chemical sensors** – measure changes in **gases** (carbon dioxide and sulphur dioxide) which can indicate magma activity below the ground (for example, Mageik, Alaska).

Even with the use of this technology, we still cannot accurately predict the exact time when volcanic eruptions or earthquakes will occur. However, they can help warn us of imminent hazards.

## Worked example

**FOUNDN C**

The picture shows an instrument used to help predict earthquakes.

1 What is the instrument called?

☐ **A** laser
☒ **B** seismometer
☐ **C** satellite image
☐ **D** chemical sensor

2 Tiltmeters are used to help predict volcanic eruptions. Describe how they can do this. **(2 marks)**

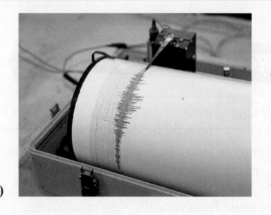

Tiltmeters measure 'bulges' or changes in the slope of volcanoes. This could mean that magma or gas is trying to escape, which could result in a volcanic eruption.

Check that you understand what different instruments measure when trying to predict volcanic eruptions or earthquakes.

## Now try this

**HIGHER C**

Suggest ways in which prediction can help reduce the effects of an earthquake. **(3 marks)**

It is useful if you use examples of instruments which can help predict earthquakes **and** volcanic eruptions.

# A world of waste

Waste is any substance or object that someone throws away. High-income countries (HICs) and low-income countries (LICs) produce different quantities and types of waste. You need to know about domestic waste, especially in HICs.

## What is waste?

There are many different types of waste.

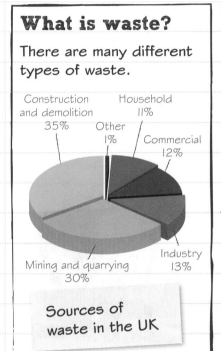

Sources of waste in the UK

## Waste in HICs and LICs

Domestic waste

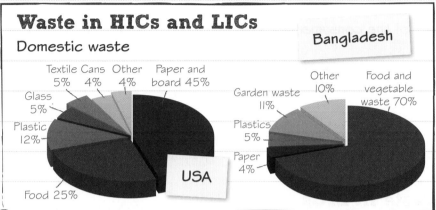

Bangladesh

USA

## More or less

HICs produce four times more waste than LICs.

• LICs typically produce 100–200 kg per person per year. Laos produces 237 kg per person per year.

• HICs typically produce 400–800 kg per person per year – Ireland, Norway, USA and Denmark produce most.

It is sometimes harder to calculate waste for LICs.

## Worked example

HIGHER C-B

Write down the amount of waste produced by at least three different countries in your answer.

Make sure you write a sentence comparing the amounts in each country.

1  Look at Figure 1. Which country produces the greatest amount of waste?  **(1 mark)**
France

2  Describe the differences in waste production shown on Figure 1. Use waste production data in your answer.  **(3 marks)**

In general, HICs produce more waste than LICs – France produces 57 million tonnes whereas Ethiopia has 1 million tonnes. However, in Africa, Morocco produces the most waste with nearly 10 million tonnes.

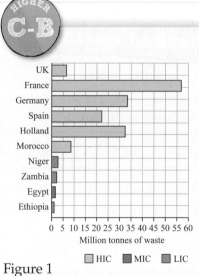

Figure 1

## Now try this

The amount of household waste shown on the graph is for a person living in a high-income country (HIC). Suggest why.  **(2 marks)**

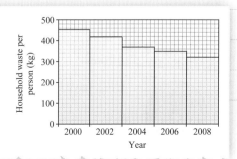

# Wealth and waste

The amount of waste that a country generates can be linked to its **wealth**.

## Waste in HICs

As a country becomes wealthier, the demand for consumer products increases. It becomes part of the **consumer society**. Many HICs can now be called **throwaway societies**.

> The richer we are, the more **disposable income** we have ➤

> We can buy more products and replace them more frequently ➤

> Waste is created by the old product and the packaging for the replacement

## Waste in LICs

LICs produce only a small quantity of waste. The type of waste produced is very different from waste in HICs. There are many reasons for this:

- Purchases are limited due to low incomes.
- Little packaging is used, so there is little plastic waste.
- Fewer people can read, so there are fewer newspapers.
- People rarely use disposable nappies and single-use drinks cans.
- Practical recycling is popular for personal use.

In LICs people recycle for personal use.

## Worked example

**E-D**

Complete the sentences to suggest why people in high-income countries (HICs) create a lot of waste.
Use some of the words in the box below.          **(5 marks)**

> MICs   ~~HICs~~   LICs   ~~food~~   ~~plastic~~   garden   ~~packaging~~   glass   waste

People in ___HICs___ have more money.
This means that they are able to buy products which come with lots of ___packaging___ .
This can lead to ___plastic___ and paper waste.
People in HICs can easily buy ___food___ from supermarkets.
Often people buy more than they can eat, leading to ___waste___ .

> ◄ Make sure that you read the text after the gap so that you have a fuller understanding of the content.
>
> Cross through the words in the text box when you use them to make sure you do not duplicate your answers.

## Now try this

HICs have been described as 'throwaway societies'. Explain why.          **(4 marks)**

# Domestic waste in HICs

HICs commonly produce a lot of **domestic** waste. This can be divided into three categories.

## 1 Electronic waste

This includes electronic goods, like mobile phones and computers, which are discarded early in their use for updated versions. The United Nations estimates that 50 million tonnes of these goods are produced each year.

**Mobile phones**
- 15 million mobiles are disposed of every year.
- They contain harmful chemicals such as cadmium and mercury.
- There are more than 5 billion mobiles on the planet!

## 2 White goods

These products include domestic **appliances** commonly used in the home, e.g. fridges, freezers, dishwashers and washing machines.

## 3 Packaging

The UK produced 10.5 million tonnes of packaging in 2007, 70% was for food and drink.

There are three main types:

- **primary** – wrapping / containers handled by consumers
- **secondary** – larger boxes or cases for distribution
- **transit** – pallets, cardboard and plastic wrapping used to load and transport goods.

**Plastics** are popular for packaging as they are robust, energy-efficient and light.

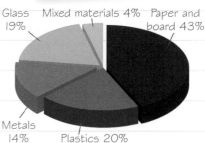

Weight of packaging material

Packaging often contains a mixture of different products and this can make it difficult to recycle.

---

## Worked example

| | |
|---|---|
| Garden | 24% |
| Kitchen | 18% |
| Paper and board | 16% |
| Glass | 8% |
| Plastic | 8% |
| White goods | 6% |
| Other | 20% |

Study the table, which shows the different types of waste produced in 2006 in one country.

**1** Does this country seem to be an HIC or LIC? **(1 mark)**

HIC

**2** Suggest **two** reasons for your answer. **(2 marks)**

There are 6% white goods such as dishwashers and washing machines, which in low-income countries would be rare. Also, HICs have more disposable income so can afford to buy more products which produce a lot of packaging waste, such as plastic and paper.

Try to **refer** to the data in the table, even when the question has not directly asked you to.

---

## Now try this

What does the term **recycling** mean? **(1 mark)**

# Recycling waste locally

## Waste hierarchy

Recycling is a more **sustainable** way of dealing with waste and is an important part of the waste hierarchy.

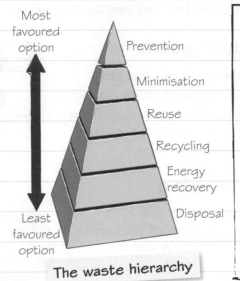

Most favoured option

Prevention
Minimisation
Reuse
Recycling
Energy recovery
Disposal

Least favoured option

The waste hierarchy

### Benefits of recycling

- Saves energy, reducing **greenhouse gases**.
- Uses less energy than producing goods from scratch.
- Reduces the demand for raw materials.
- Lessens the impact of **extracting** (mining, quarrying and logging) and transporting raw materials.
- Reduces the amount of waste going to **landfill** or **incinerators**.

## Worked example

Outline **three** advantages of recycling. **(3 marks)**

1  Uses less energy than producing the product from scratch.
2  Decreases the demand for raw materials.
3  Helps reduce the amount of waste which goes to landfill.

The question asks you to **outline**, so you do not need to **explain** your answers.

## Now try this

The map shows the percentage for recycling rates for Greater London.

1  Which Greater London borough has the highest recycling rate? **(1 mark)**

☐ **A** Croydon
☐ **B** Barnet
☐ **C** Bexley
☐ **D** Brent

2  How many Greater London boroughs have a recycling rate below 24%? **(1 mark)**

☐ **A** 8
☐ **B** 9
☐ **C** 15
☐ **D** 16

N

Enfield

Barnet

Harrow

Haringey
Waltham Forest
Redbridge
Havering

Hillingdon

Brent
Islington
Hackney
City of Westminster
Tower Hamlets
Newham
Barkingham & Dagenham

Ealing
K & C
H & F

River Thames

Hounslow
Southwark
Lambeth
Greenwich
Bexley

Richmond upon Thames
Wandsworth
Lewisham

Kingston upon Thames
Merton

River Thames
Sutton
Croydon
Bromley

**Key**
■ Above 40%
☐ 31–40%
▨ 24–30%
☐ Below 24%
C  City
K & C  Kensington & Chelsea
H & F  Hammersmith & Fulham

When the question is about a map, it is very important that you **look** at the key carefully. With question 2, make sure you tick off the boroughs on the map as you count – this way you won't miscount.

# Recycling waste locally: Camden

The London Borough of Camden has a population of 217 000 with 97 000 households which generate 72 000 tonnes of waste per year.

**Case study**

You need to know a case study of recycling on a local scale.

## Camden: successes so far

- In 2007, recycling in Camden was 27% compared to 17% in 2003/04.
- Twice-weekly collection of household waste is sent to the **Energy from Waste** (EfW) incinerator at Edmonton or to **landfills** in Bedfordshire.
- A doorstep recycling scheme operates weekly by Veolia.
- Regis Road Recycling Centre has increased from 58% (2004) to 70% (2008). It was upgraded in 2007 to allow recycling of more products (plasterboard and plastics) and to make it safer and more pleasant.
- Large recycling bins have been placed in three parks in Camden.
- Recycling advisers now operate in schools and on housing estates.
- Camden was the first authority in the country to trial recycling of batteries.

## What happens to all the recycling in Camden?

**Paper and card** are taken to Taplow, Maidenhead and made into paper products.

**Glass, cans and plastic** are sent to a MRF facility in Bromley by Bow, East London. They are sorted into material **types** and reprocessed in the UK and abroad. Glass bottles and jars are crushed into sand and used in buildings, pavements and roads. Plastics are made into planter pots or recycling bins. Metals remade into metal products.

**Food and garden waste** goes to an industrial composting facility in north London. It is shredded and put in composting tunnels for 12 weeks, then used in agricultural and horticultural outlets.

## Worked example

Complete the sentences to describe how recycled products can be used.     **(5 marks)**

more ~~sand~~ ~~road~~ ~~plastic~~ ~~fewer~~ edible ~~toilet~~ mud

Using recycled materials means that ___fewer___ natural resources are used. Recycled paper can be used to make ___toilet___ paper. Recycled glass is used for ___road___ building. It can also be turned into ___sand___ for golf bunkers. Pens can be made from recycled ___plastic___ cups.

## Now try this

Choose **one** study of recycling on a local scale.
Explain how waste is recycled and how recycled material is used.     **(6 marks + 4 marks SPaG )**

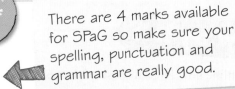

There are 4 marks available for SPaG so make sure your spelling, punctuation and grammar are really good.

# Waste disposal in HICs

High-income countries (HICs) dispose of waste in different ways. Germany produces about 40 million tonnes of domestic waste every year. It uses three main methods to dispose of this waste.

> **Case study**
>
> You need to know a case study of the ways in which an HIC disposes of its waste.

## Waste disposal in Germany

**1  Landfill**

Germany has impermeable geology, so waste can be buried in the holes created by mining and mineral extraction.

✓ The process is relatively cheap.

✓ It can be used for nuclear waste.

> Space is running out – Germany exports around 2 million tonnes of non-hazardous waste to China and Spain.

**2  Incineration**

Rubbish is burned in incinerators. Fuel bricks for energy can also be created from shredded waste. This is called **Electricity from Waste** (EfW).

✓ Modern incinerators are clean.

✓ Electricity or heat can be generated for homes.

✗ The waste is linked to cancer, rashes and nose bleeds.

✗ Carbon emissions are produced.

**3  Recycling**

Germany has developed a 'green dot' scheme. Manufacturers have to pay all recycling costs if they don't join the scheme.

✓ This has reduced waste by 1 million tonnes per year.

✓ 60% of all household waste is recycled in Germany.

✗ Germany can deal with only one-third of own recycling.

✗ It is expensive ($30 per person).

## Worked example

Explain how **one** high-income country (HIC) disposes of its waste.   **(4 marks)**

Germany creates 40 million tonnes of domestic waste per year and disposes of it in three ways. They use EfW to create electricity and heat which is then used to heat local homes as well as use within the incinerator plant. Germany also uses landfill; however this method is decreasing because Germany is running out of space. As a result of this they actually ship around 2 million tonnes of waste to Spain and China. 60% of all household waste is recycled in Germany, and in some areas such as Bavaria the percentage is even higher (67%). Germany has introduced the green dot scheme, which manufacturers use to help increase recycling. This has helped Germany reduce its overall household waste by 1 million tonnes per year.

> Make clear, concise points and back them up with facts from a case study you know.

## Now try this

Outline how HICs dispose of domestic waste.   **(3 marks)**

# Non-renewable energy

**Non-renewable** energy sources are fuels which cannot be remade or regrown, such as coal or gas. You will need to know the advantages and disadvantages of **one** of these energy sources.

**Case study**

You need to know a case study of a non-renewable energy source.

## Oil in Ecuador

Shell, then later Chevron-Texaco, started drilling for oil in Oriente area of Ecuador (13 million hectares of tropical rainforest).

Local people of Oriente filed a lawsuit against oil companies for damage to their environment.

Texaco signed a deal for $40 million for a clean up operation but this was not enough to cover whole cost.

Chevron told by court to pay $48 bn for environmental damage.

1930 | 1937 1940 | 1950 | 1960 | 1970 1993 | 1980 | 1990 1995 | 2000 2011 | 2013

### Positive impacts

✓ Economy of Ecuador grew on average 7% annually. Oil created 40% of national export earnings.

✓ Income per capita increased from $290 in 1972 to $8500 in 2011.

✓ New roads opened up remote regions.

✓ Oil was seen as a way to solve the national debt, which was $256 million in 1970.

### Negative impacts

✗ Large-scale deforestation.

✗ Indigenous tribes such as the Huaoroni and Secoya were forcibly displaced.

✗ Little revenue was fed back into the local community.

✗ Pipelines leaked 38000 litres of oil every week. 30 major spills were recorded.

✗ Aquatic life was harmed by the reduction in dissolved oxygen.

✗ Contaminated water led to skin rashes and cancer.

✗ Burning waste led to toxic air particles and 'black rain', increasing greenhouse gas emissions.

**Worked example**  FOUND'N E-D

Figure 1 is a cartoon about a source of energy.
Describe **two** disadvantages of the source of energy shown in Figure 1.

**(2 marks)**

When oil is burned it can release large amounts of carbon dioxide. This is a greenhouse gas and can contribute to global warming. In transporting the oil, spills can also occur.

Figure 1

**Now try this** HIGHER C

With the aid of an example, outline the advantages and disadvantages of using a non-renewable energy source.

**(4 marks)**

# Renewable energy

**Renewable energy** sources are infinite. Electricity can be generated from solar, wind, wave, tidal and hydroelectric power (HEP).

**Case study**

You need to know a case study of a renewable energy source, its advantages and disadvantages.

## Wind power in the UK

The UK has the biggest wind resource in Europe. In 2010 the government announced a £75 billion programme to build onshore and offshore wind farms.

Energy production from renewable sources in the UK increased by 33% in 2010. With wind power, there was a 45% increase from **onshore wind** (ONW) and 68% from **offshore wind** (OFFW).

### Positive impacts

✓ OFFW predicted to meet the UK's current energy demand 10 times over.

✓ Becoming cheaper source of energy as technology advances.

✓ By 2020, UK will have 15% of energy needs from wind power.

✓ Reduces carbon footprint and climate change.

### Negative impacts

✗ ONW farms can result in a loss of 2–3 hectares of land per turbine.

✗ Decline in bats and sea birds is possible – a proposed wind farm at Docking Shoal, Lincolnshire was declined because of this risk.

✗ Hydraulic hammers create high levels of underwater sound and can harm wildlife.

✗ Noise and visual pollution.

✗ Expensive – a large turbine can cost over £3 million.

Wind farm installed capacities (MW)

Onshore
- · <5
- · 5–10
- · 10–20
- · 20–30
- · 30–40
- · >40

Offshore
- · <10
- · 10–100
- · 100–500
- · >500

Wind farms in the UK

---

## Worked example

**FOUNDN D**

Figure 1 is a cartoon about a source of energy.

1 Which type of fuel is shown in Figure 1? **(1 mark)**

☐ **A** nuclear    ☐ **C** coal power
☒ **B** renewable    ☐ **D** non-renewable

2 Describe **two** disadvantages of the source of energy shown in Figure 1. **(2 marks)**

Wind farms can be noisy and can upset the migration patterns of birds. Often birds fly into them and they can be killed.

That's it! Next time I'm walking.

Figure 1

---

## Now try this

**HIGHER C**

1 What message is the cartoon in the Worked example trying to give? **(2 marks)**

2 Outline the benefits of the type of energy shown in the cartoon. **(3 marks)**

# Energy deficit and surplus

Most countries have a balanced energy usage – they create enough energy to meet demand. Countries that use more energy than they create have an **energy deficit**. Countries that create more then they use have an **energy surplus**.

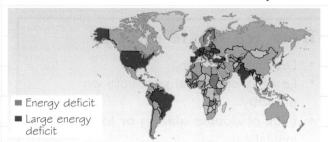

- ■ Energy deficit
- ■ Large energy deficit

- ■ Energy surplus
- ■ Large energy surplus

HICs in general have a deficit of energy.

Many LICs have a surplus of energy.

## Trends and variations

Energy consumption can **vary** for many reasons. The diagram shows the general trend in energy consumption – a rich country with a high population and an available energy source will have a high energy consumption.

| Higher | Energy consumption | Lower |

Population

Wealth GDP

Availability of energy sources

However, not all countries or regions conform to the pattern.

General trend in energy consumption

## Worked example

HIGHER C-B

Key
■ Surplus
■ Balance
■ Deficit

Describe the distribution of energy use in Europe. Use evidence from the map in your answer. **(3 marks)**

Energy use is not evenly distributed. There are only two surplus nations – UK and Norway. There are also only two that have an energy balance (Denmark and Belgium). The remainder of Europe has an energy deficit.

This is an excellent answer, using map evidence and noting uneven distribution as well as exceptions to the trend.

## Now try this

FOUNDN E

An energy deficit is when countries:                                   **(1 mark)**

☐ **A** produce as much energy as they use            ☐ **C** produce more energy than they use

☐ **B** use more energy than they produce            ☐ **D** sell all of the energy they produce

# Wasting our energy

As countries become more developed, their consumption of energy increases. However, in many HICs energy is **wasted** in the home and at work. Britain is one of the highest energy wasters in Europe.

## Wasting energy at home

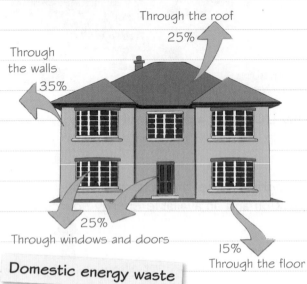

Through the roof
25%

Through the walls
35%

25%
Through windows and doors

15%
Through the floor

Domestic energy waste

### How we waste energy

- Leaving lights on.
- Leaving electrical products on standby.
- Lack of double glazing or loft / wall insulation.
- Setting thermostats too high.
- Leaving windows and doors open.
- Leaving mobile chargers plugged in.

It is estimated that Britons can save £350 per year by being more energy efficient.

## Wasting energy at work

Leaks from compressed air valves mean machinery must work harder and use more fuel

Printers, computers and fax machines left on – wastes £8 million per year

Inefficient fuel use in steel industry – heat wasted as exhaust or flue gases

Energy wastage from offices and industry approximately £12 billion a year

Vibrations in machinery that is not level or stable, waste energy

Machinery poorly serviced or maintained – becomes inefficient and uses more fuel

## Worked example

FOUNDN
E-D

Describe **three** ways in which energy is wasted in the home. **(3 marks)**

We waste large amounts of energy in the home. Most energy is lost through the roof (45%) with the windows and doors being the next highest (35%) – this is increased even more if there is no double glazing. Many people leave their lights on which wastes energy and many leave their TVs on standby rather than switching them off – this all wastes energy.

## EXAM ALERT!

Try to include some accurate statistics to help support the statements.

Students have struggled with exam questions similar to this – **be prepared!**  ResultsPlus

Try not to just list the reasons why, include some description as well.

## Now try this

HIGHER
C

Outline how offices and industries waste energy. **(3 marks)**

# Carbon footprints

Countries at different levels of development have different carbon footprints. An HIC is likely to have a higher carbon footprint than an LIC, due to greater use of energy for example.

## What is a carbon footprint?

It is a measurement of all the **greenhouse gases (GHGs)** individuals contribute to our environment as a result of our daily lives. For example, 14% recreation and leisure, 12% home electricity.

## How is it measured?

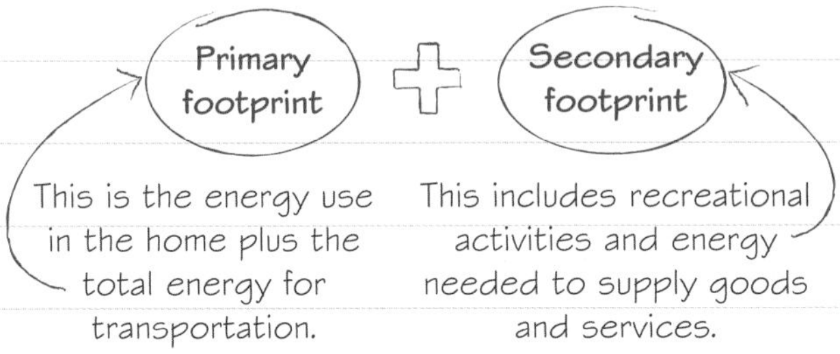

Primary footprint ⊕ Secondary footprint

This is the energy use in the home plus the total energy for transportation.

This includes recreational activities and energy needed to supply goods and services.

A carbon footprint is written as kilograms (kg) of the **equivalent carbon dioxide** per person. The world average is 4000 kg, and the target to fight climate change is 2000 kg.

## Country to country

A country's carbon footprint is usually expressed as equivalent carbon dioxide per capita – the total GHGs emitted divided by its population. For example, the USA has a carbon footprint of 17 300 kg per person, China 5800 kg per person and Ethiopia just 100 kg per person whilst Qatar has a carbon footprint of 44 000 kg per person.

- Countries with higher carbon footprints tend to be richer and more industrialised – HICs.
- Countries with medium carbon footprints tend to be emerging countries increasing their industry – MICs.
- Countries with low carbon footprints tend to be poorer and less industrialised – LICs.

## Climate conferences

Target setting at **climate conferences** (Kyoto, Japan, 1997 and Durban, South Africa, 2011) aimed to decrease carbon footprints.

## Worked example

**HIGHER C**

1  Complete Figure 1 for recreation and commuting. Use the data in the table below. **(2 marks)**

| Activity | MtCO$_2$ |
|----------|----------|
| Recreation | 116 |
| Commuting | 48 |

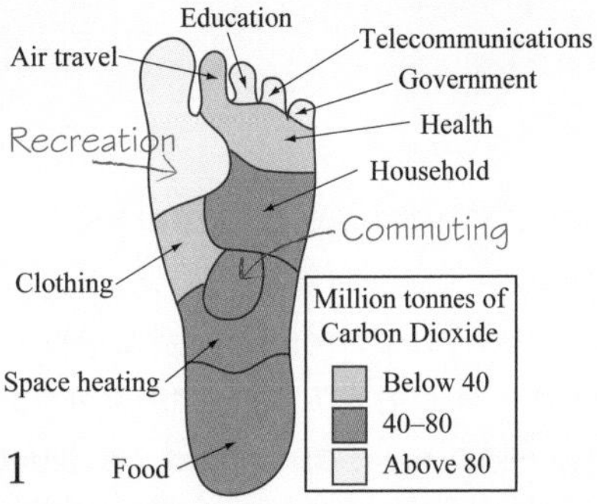

Education, Air travel, Telecommunications, Government, Health, Recreation, Household, Commuting, Clothing, Space heating, Food

Million tonnes of Carbon Dioxide
Below 40
40–80
Above 80

Figure 1

2  State the values of MtCO$_2$ for air travel and household. **(2 marks)**

Air travel – below 40 MtCO$_2$
Household – 40–80 MtCO$_2$

Make sure that you read the information in the key carefully.

## Now try this

**FOUNDN E**

What is a carbon footprint? **(1 mark)**

☐ **A**  a large footprint made of carbon
☐ **B**  the amount of carbon used per person
☐ **C**  the amount of carbon stored in the Earth
☐ **D**  the amount of carbon dioxide breathed out per person

# Energy efficiency

The key to solving energy wastage is to be more **energy efficient**. There are many ways to do this at different levels – **domestic**, **local** and **national**.

## Domestic solutions

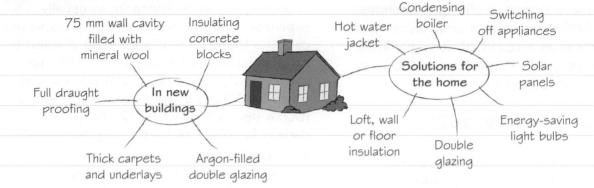

- 75 mm wall cavity filled with mineral wool
- Insulating concrete blocks
- Full draught proofing
- In new buildings
- Thick carpets and underlays
- Argon-filled double glazing

- Condensing boiler
- Switching off appliances
- Hot water jacket
- Solutions for the home
- Solar panels
- Loft, wall or floor insulation
- Double glazing
- Energy-saving light bulbs

## Local solutions

The Eastcroft District Housing Scheme in Nottingham uses the steam generated by waste incineration to provide heating and electricity for thousands of home. The scheme has advantages and disadvantages:

👍 reduces waste sent to landfill

👍 recycles metal (3000 tonnes of iron and steel) and ash

👍 emissions filtered so they are less harmful

👎 harmful gases released during production

👎 may discourage waste reduction

👎 expensive – costs £1 million / year

👎 emissions not monitored.

## National solutions

The government aims to reduce their EHG emissions by 30% by 2020:

- reducing tax to 85% for companies that meet climate change **targets**
- funding the Carbon Trust which provides **education**, advice and help
- trialling 'smart' energy **meters** in some businesses
- introducing new **building regulations**
- encouraging the use of renewable energy sources such as solar and wind power.

## Worked example

**D**

Describe **two** ways to reduce domestic energy wastage.   **(4 marks)**

People in their homes could save energy by using energy saving light bulbs and by turning off appliances instead of leaving them on standby – this is one of the major causes of energy waste in the UK, as the appliance still uses electricity even when on standby. Also houses could be built with energy-efficient materials such as insulation blocks for walls to keep in heat; and the use of argon in double glazing would stop heat escaping.

Highlight the key words in the question to help you focus on what the question wants you to do.

## Now try this

**C**

Explain how the UK can reduce its energy wastage.   **(6 marks + 4 marks SPaG)**

This question has not indicated the scale, so you could choose to cover domestic, local or national issues and includes examples. Make sure you check your spelling, punctuation and grammar.

# Water consumption

The economic development of a country will influence the amount of water it consumes. You need to know how the water **consumption** between HICs and LICs differs.

## HICs and LICs

Average water consumption is an expression of the total water used in a country divided by its population. HIC water consumption is high. On average, every person uses 1200m³ per year. This is three times more than LICs (400m³ per person per year).

- Agriculture
- Industry
- Domestic

HIC water consumption

LIC water consumption

## How water is used in HICs and LICs

|        | Agriculture | Domestic | Industry |
|--------|-------------|----------|----------|
| HICs | Drip feed sprinklers for watering crops control amount of water used; Automated irrigation systems use lots of water | Piped water means people use lots of water for: • domestic appliances • baths and showers • toilets; Recreational use, e.g. swimming pools, hot tubs | Water used for cooling machinery in factories |
| LICs | Ineffective irrigation Hand pumps limit water use; Surplus water left to drain away, evaporate or run off surface | 11% of world's population lack access to clean water supply. • Communal taps and wells used for washing clothes • Bathe in rivers | Small-scale industries, e.g. basket weaving and pottery, use very little water |

Key  = low water use    = high water use

 **Worked example** F-E

State **two** ways in which water can be used in the home. **(2 marks)**

Water can be used in the home in many ways. It is most commonly used for showering or baths and for flushing the toilet.

The command word is **state** so you don't need to explain.

 **Now try this** C

The pie chart shows the use of domestic water in Canada (HIC). Complete the pie chart using the data in the table. **(2 marks)**

| Water usage | (%) |
|-------------|-----|
| Kitchen and drinking | 10 |
| Shower and bath | 35 |
| Cleaning | 5 |

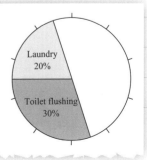
Laundry 20%
Toilet flushing 30%

# Rising water use

As a country becomes wealthier and more developed, its demand for water increases. You need to know the reasons for increased demand and how this is affected by development.

## Increasing demand

- Asia experienced a steady rise from 1900, and then a rapid increase from 1950 onwards.
- North America and Europe experienced a small increase in the early 1970s, and then remained fairly stable.
- Africa and South America have lower water consumption, but experienced a slight increase in the early 1970s.
- Oceania and Australia have the lowest water consumption by continent, and there is little change.

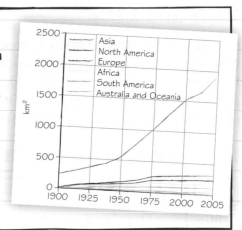

## Reasons for the pattern

As a country develops, the **standard of living** also increases. This leads to:

**1** greater **mechanisation** in industry, using more water for manufacture (food and drink) and to cool down machinery

**2** more **labour-saving devices** – washing machines use 80 litres of water per wash and dishwashers use 35 litres of water per wash

**3** more water used for washing cars and watering gardens, and for luxuries like swimming pools and hot tubs

**4** increased personal hygiene – we have moved towards **a showering society**, where people have regular showers, using 8 litres of water per day

**5** increased leisure and tourism, with more water used in water parks, spas and watering golf courses.

## Worked example

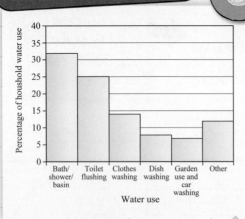

The percentages of household water use shown by the graph are for people living in an HIC. Suggest why. **(2 marks)**

Accessibility to water is much better in HICs. People can use this water in appliances such as dishwashers and washing machines. Car ownership in LICs is limited and so people use less water to wash them than in HICs, so the graph is not for an LIC.

With a question like this, you can explain either why LICs have lower water consumption or why HICs have higher water consumption.

## Now try this

HICs are described as 'showering societies'. Explain why. **(4 marks)**

# Local water sources

There are three main local water sources; **reservoirs**, **rivers** and **aquifers**. Reservoirs are artificial lakes created by building a dam across a river. Water can be taken directly from rivers. Aquifers are areas of **permeable** or **porous** rocks below the surface that can hold water in tiny pores, e.g. Chiltern Hills and North Downs.

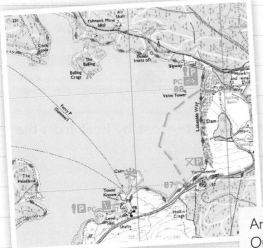

## Kielder Water Reservoir, Northumberland

Planned in the 1960s, Kielder is the largest artificial lake in the UK and holds 200 billion litres of water. It supplies nearby large settlements (Newcastle, Sunderland and Middlesbrough). In the Kielder Transfer Scheme, water is moved from the Tyne to the Wear and Tees during water shortages. The reservoir also offers many leisure opportunities.

Another example of a water transfer scheme is the Ely Ouse-Essex Water Transfer scheme which transfers water from areas of surplus water supply to areas of low supply.

## Peace River, Florida, USA

- Water from Peace River supports 750 000 people.
- 70 million litres per day are extracted.
- Impurities are removed at a water treatment plant near Fort Ogden.
- Treated water is injected into an aquifer for storage (**aquifer storage and recovery**) to help with seasonal water demands.

## London aquifer

- 20% of London's water comes from boreholes linked to **groundwater** supplies.
- 80% of London's water comes from storage reservoirs connected to the River Thames and River Lee.
- Water rises under hydrostatic pressure.
- Extraction rates can impact on the water table, e.g. in 1960s increased industrial activity lowered the water table.
- Extraction is now less and the high water table can cause subsidence and damage to tall buildings, so extraction can be increased to avoid this.

## Worked example

**D**

The photograph shows Kielder Water, a reservoir in Northumberland.

What is a reservoir? **(2 marks)**

A reservoir is a natural or artificial lake used as part of a water supply system.

Make sure you learn your key terms.

## Now try this

**B**

Explain how an aquifer can be used as a source of water. **(4 marks)**

# Water surplus and deficit

There are areas of the world that have a water **surplus** and areas where there is a water **deficit**. You need to know the relationship between rainfall distribution and water deficit and surplus.

## Water budget

Water budget is the relationship between the input and output of water in a region. It is linked to three factors:

 **1** rainfall

Global water surplus and deficit

Water deficit — Water surplus

 **2** transpiration (how water moves up a plant to the surface)

 **3** evaporation (water lost by heat from the Sun).

## World rainfall distribution

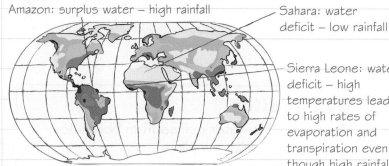

Amazon: surplus water – high rainfall

Sahara: water deficit – low rainfall

Sierra Leone: water deficit – high temperatures lead to high rates of evaporation and transpiration even though high rainfall

Average annual precipitation mm

■3000 ▣2000 ▣1000 ▢500 ▢250 ▢below 250

Don't assume that areas with high rainfall will have a water surplus, while areas with low rainfall will have a deficit. Include references to rates of evapo-transpiration and what will impact on these (for example, amount / type of vegetation, temperature).

## Worked example

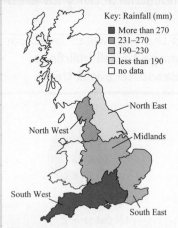

Key: Rainfall (mm)
■ More than 270
▣ 231–270
▣ 190–230
▢ less than 190
▢ no data

North East, North West, Midlands, South West, South East

Figure 1

Study Figure 1. It shows a map of rainfall distribution in England for winter 2009.

Describe the distribution of rainfall in England shown on Figure 1. Use rainfall data in your answer. **(3 marks)**

In the west of England rainfall is exceptionally high with more than 270 mm per year until you hit the Midlands and SE where the rainfall falls below average (190–230 mm per year). In the NE, there is an extreme lack of rainfall (190 mm per year). Overall, the west receives more than the east.

Try to include data shown on the map and summarise the overall trend.

## Now try this

Water surpluses are likely to occur in areas with:
☐ **A** high rainfall and high temperatures
☐ **B** low rainfall and high temperatures
☐ **C** high rainfall and low temperatures
☐ **D** low rainfall and low temperatures   **(1 mark)**

# Water supply problems: HICs

The availability and supply of clean water can cause problems.

Old pipes cannot cope with increased water pressure, e.g. London

Loss from broken / old pipes

Quality — Fertilisers, industrial leakages and sewage treatment may cause water pollution

**Water supply problems: HICs**

Seasonal variability

Spatial variability

Low rainfall at peak times, e.g. tourist industry in southern Europe

High rainfall occuring in less populated areas, e.g. upland areas

## Worked example

**HIGHER C**

Study Figure 1. It shows water supply problems in England.

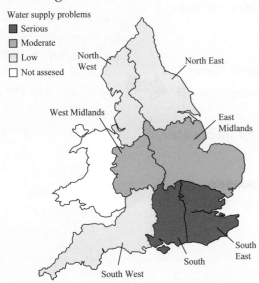

Water supply problems
- ■ Serious
- ■ Moderate
- ☐ Low
- ☐ Not assesed

North West, North East, West Midlands, East Midlands, South West, South, South East

Figure 1

**1** Name a region with low water supply problems in England. **(1 mark)**

SW

**2** Describe the distribution of water supply problems in England. Use evidence from Figure 1 in your answer. **(4 marks)**

From the map, serious water supply problems seem to occur most towards the south and east of the map. The most serious issues are in the south and south-east, whereas the north-west and north-east are both low. The East and West Midlands are 'moderate', and it is only the south-west region with its low status which disrupts the north (low) and south (serious) pattern. This suggests that the further east, the more severe the supply problem.

Remember – in a **describe** question you do not need to **explain**.

## Now try this

**FOUNDN D**

Look at the map in the Worked example.

Suggest reasons why some regions have serious water supply problems. **(3 marks)**

This question expects you to relate your answer to the map, so it is important that you look at the resource carefully.

# Water supply problems: LICs

The problems associated with water supply are generally more serious in LICs than HICs.

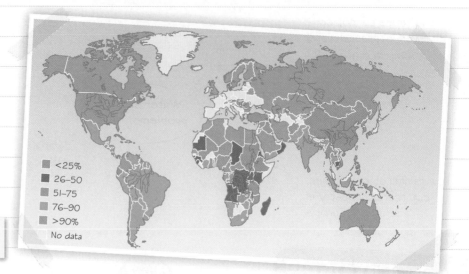

| <25% |
| 26–50 |
| 51–75 |
| 76–90 |
| >90% |
| No data |

Access to safe water

## Water availability and cleanliness

A lack of available water affects more than 1 billion people. Women and children may spend up to 8 hours a day collecting water from sources that are often polluted.

**Water pollution** is caused by:

* the results of deforestation – sediment runs into rivers
* poor farming methods – fertilisers and pesticides run off into water courses
* mining and industry – dangerous chemicals seep into water courses.

Pollution can either be from one source **point-source pollution**, or from many different sources (**non-point pollution**).

A lack of clean water can lead to **water-borne diseases**, e.g. cholera, bilharzia and typhoid, affect approximately 900 million people with 3.4 million dying every year.

3000 died of cholera in Zimbabwe in 2008–2009.

## Worked example

Describe how a lack of clean water can lead to an increase in diseases such as cholera. **(2 marks)**

Dirty water can lead to more diseases such as cholera and typhoid. This is because germs will live in the water and make it a water-borne disease.

### EXAM ALERT!

Be careful that you don't repeat the question in your answer. You must link dirty water to increased chances of getting diseases such as cholera.

Students have struggled with exam questions similar to this – **be prepared!**  ResultsPlus

## Now try this

Explain **two** water supply problems in Low Income Countries. **(4 marks)**

Make sure you use two different problems as the question specifies.

# Managing water in HICs

Water is used in many different ways: **domestic**, **industrial** and **agricultural**. You need to know how a NIC might manage water use.

## Ways with water

| Domestic | Industrial | Agriculture |
|---|---|---|
|  <br> • Water meters – people pay for what they use <br> • Dual flush toilets – reduce water used <br> • Hosepipe bans – when there are drought conditions, e.g. April 2012 |  <br> • Reuse of water from cooling process, e.g. in steel industry has reduced waste consumption by 60% over 10 years (Tata Steel India) <br> • Reduction of pollutants in water, e.g. at Cwm Rheidol zinc mine cockleshells, limestone and compost are used to clean the water that is discharged from the flooded abandoned mines before it reaches the river Rheidol |  <br> Drip feed sprinkler systems used to irrigate crops which are more efficient than ditches |

## Worked example

Explain how HICs manage their usage of water in industry and agriculture. **(4 marks)**

Tata Steel in India recycles water by using micro-organisms that help decompose pollutants. This helps clean the wastewater which is then reused in the plant.

In agriculture, farmers commonly use sprinklers (which use 75 litres of water per second) and channels or ditches. Water usage has been reduced by using drip-feed sprinklers, which are 90% more efficient and so help conserve water. In some areas, rainwater harvesting has also been used.

This is an excellent answer, which has clear focus and specific facts on both the industrial and agricultural management of water.

## Now try this

Water can be managed effectively for agricultural purposes.

1 Which of these agricultural uses wastes least water? **(1 mark)**
☐ **A** 24-hour sprinklers
☐ **B** using a hosepipe for 18 hours
☐ **C** drip irrigation which waters plants when needed
☐ **D** watering with 500 buckets a day

2 Which of the following will help reduce water use in the home? **(1 mark)**
☐ **A** having a bath
☐ **B** leaving the tap running while brushing your teeth
☐ **C** dripping taps
☐ **D** using a dual-flush toilet

Had a look ☐  Nearly there ☐  Nailed it! ☐

# Managing water in LICs

In LICs water management generally involves the use of **appropriate technology**. This involves small-scale equipment or schemes that are run by local people, are environmentally friendly and promote sustainability.

## Cost-effective boreholes (CEBs) in Africa

Many CEBs are being planned. They:

- help small communities by giving them clean water supply, which prevents the spread of disease
- consist of basic technology that can often be maintained by people in LICs and is cost-effective
- are supported by the Rural Water Supply Network
- cost $5000–$6000 to install.

A borehole in Mozambique, one of 2000 planned, partly funded by the Dutch government

## Sustainable townships in India

- Sangamam village near Tamil Nadu, India was set up in January 2008. Sustainability is the key to the development of this new area and water management is a particular focus.
- Rainwater is harvested through roof-top containers. This water is used for flushing the toilet and watering the garden.
- The organic parts of sewage (solid waste) are composted and re-used as garden manure. The rest is then treated through an anaerobic process and re-used on the garden or for flushing toilets.
- Storm water is collected and stored in unlined ponds, which are then used to recharge groundwater supplies and for encouraging fish farming.
- Houses in the township have three pipes into their homes. One is for underground water supply, another is for harvested rainwater and the third is for treated wastewater.

## Worked example

What is appropriate technology?          (1 mark)

☐ **A** building large-scale projects such as dams
☒ **B** small-scale schemes set up by the local community
☐ **C** importing water from HICs
☐ **D** high-technology water pumps

Many students feel that these questions are very easy. However silly mistakes can be made if you answer too quickly.

Read through all the options carefully before marking the one you think is correct.

## Now try this

Explain how low-income countries (LICs) use appropriate technology to provide water for small communities.          (4 marks)

Make sure you know the difference between appropriate technology and other water provision schemes.

# Managing water with dams

**Case study**

You need to know a case study that shows how water transfer can cause conflicts between two or more areas.

## River Colorado

The River Colorado Basin is 630000 km² in volume. It drains a huge area, from Wyoming in the NE to Arizona and California in the SW. All three states are competing for the water for domestic, agricultural and industrial uses. This can cause **water conflict**.

The river is heavily engineered. It has many dams such as the Boulder and Parker dams. These are used to create reservoirs, to supply water for industrial, agricultural and domestic purposes and to generate HEP.

## Who uses the water?

Between 1922–1948 various agreements allocated usage of Colorado River water.

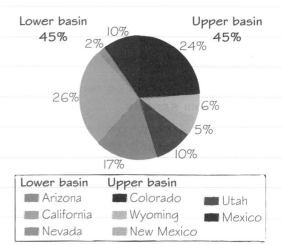

Lower basin 45%    Upper basin 45%

10%, 2%, 24%, 26%, 6%, 5%, 17%, 10%

| Lower basin | Upper basin | |
|---|---|---|
| Arizona | Colorado | Utah |
| California | Wyoming | Mexico |
| Nevada | New Mexico | |

## Problems caused by the River Colorado dam project

- Loss of land and settlements where areas are flooded behind the dams.
- Loss of habitats and wildlife when flow is reduced, e.g. desalinisation plant has affected habitats of birds (egret) and fish (totoaba).
- Mexico has been badly affected by reduced flow of water, increased pollution and salinisation of water and decrease in natural leakage into aquifers because of channels being lined, e.g. All American Canal.

Competition for water has led to disputes about the amounts of water being extracted by the different areas. The Colorado River project is now in legal controversy and all future projects have to go through an EIS (Environmental Impact Survey).

## Worked example

**FOUNDN C**

Water usage can cause conflicts. Outline the causes of such conflict in an example you have studied. **(4 marks)**

Conflict occurs when there are so many people that want to use the water from the River Colorado – local people (LA and San Diego), industry (HEP as well) and farmers (irrigation). The river has had many dams, such as the Hoover Dam and Boulder Dam to help with the demand. However, this has reduced the water that reaches Mexico, and so has limited their farming. Desalination plants have had to be built. This affects wildlife habitats, which environmental groups are upset about. The river is now under legal dispute.

Try to use an appropriate example and include case study specific detail (names of the dams and settlements).

## Now try this

Choose an example of a water management scheme you have studied. Explain the reasons for the scheme.
**(6 marks + 4 marks SPaG)**

Think about the structure of your answer as well as your spelling, punctuation and grammar.

# WRMS, Sydney

Sydney Olympic Park (SOP) was developed in 2000 to support the Olympic Games. The Water Reclamation and Management Scheme (WRMS) was set up to reduce pressure on the demand for drinking water in the Sydney area.

**Case study**

You need to know a case study of one water-management scheme, why it was necessary and its effects.

## What was involved

- a reclamation plant to remove 3 million litres per day of water from sewage
- a treatment plant to filter and disinfect 7.5 million litres per day of water from the reclamation and brick pit
- a brick pit to act as a reservoir to store 300 million litres of water from rainwater and treated sewage
- a new supply system from the treatment plant to the Olympic Park and Newington.

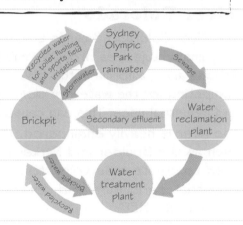

| Positives | Negatives |
|---|---|
| 👍 Saves 850 million litres of drinking water per year. | 👎 Expensive to complete – AUS$137 million. |
| 👍 Almost 100% of sewage re-used. | 👎 Developers had to consider energy conservation, waste management and protection of heritage / biodiversity. |
| 👍 Improves public confidence in recycled water. | 👎 Project had to ensure water was safe to use for domestic use. |
| 👍 Creates understanding of sustainable water use. | 👎 Difficult to overcome people's perceptions about using recycled water. |
| 👍 Supplies recycled water 15% cheaper than 'normal' drinking water. | |

## Worked example

Describe the effects on the environment of water management schemes, such as the one in the photograph. **(3 marks)**

The dam looks ugly and therefore there is visual pollution. The lake created behind the dam has caused huge amounts of land to be flooded, which could result in loss of habitat for wildlife.

Look at the photograph carefully, as many of the answers are in there – describe what you see.

**See also p. 71**

For more about dams.

## Now try this

Choose a water management scheme you have studied. Explain the effects of the scheme.
**(6 marks + 4 marks SPaG)**

# Economic sectors

As a country becomes more developed its **economic sectors** can shift.

## The three economic sectors

**1** **primary** – working with natural resources (fishing, farming, mining)

**2** **secondary** – manufacturing products (TV, car or construction)

**3** **tertiary** – providing services (shops, offices, banks, schools)

Economic sectors in HICs, MICs and LICs

HICs, e.g. USA
Tertiary
Secondary
Primary

MICs, e.g. Asia
Tertiary
Secondary
Primary

LICs, e.g. Central Africa
Tertiary
Secondary
Primary

There is also the **quaternary** sector (IT and research). This is small on a global scale but can have more significance regionally (Silicon Valley, San Francisco and the Silicon Alley along the M4 corridor, UK).

## Sector changes as countries develop

As countries become more developed and wealthier (based on their per capita **GNI** or Gross National Income), they shift through the sectors. As a result, standard of living and settlements start to grow.

Pre-industrial – Primary sector employed two-thirds of the population. Agriculture the most important activity. Jobs often much lower paid – 'dirty jobs'.

Industrial – Secondary (peaks during this phase) and tertiary increases. Primary declines.

Post-industrial – Tertiary becomes established. Primary and secondary continue to decline. Quaternary appears.

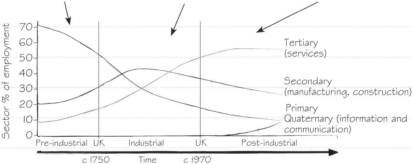

## Worked example

**FOUNDN E-D**

Look at Figure 1. It shows the changes in the employment structure of Country Z between 1970 and 2010.

In which years did the primary sector decrease the most?
**(1 mark)**

☒ **A** 1970–1980
☐ **B** 1980–1990
☐ **C** 1990–2000
☐ **D** 2000–2010

Figure 1

## Now try this

**HIGHER C**

Look at Figure 1 in the Worked example. Describe how the **primary** employment structure of Country Z has changed between 1970 and 2010. Use evidence in your answer. **(4 marks)**

Make sure you **look at the graph carefully** because the answer is on it!

# Primary sector decline

The UK has gone through economic development, and as a result has moved through the different economic sectors.

The decline in the primary industry started 250 years ago as a result of the **industrial revolution**. Today less than 2% work in primary industries.

## Why the decline?

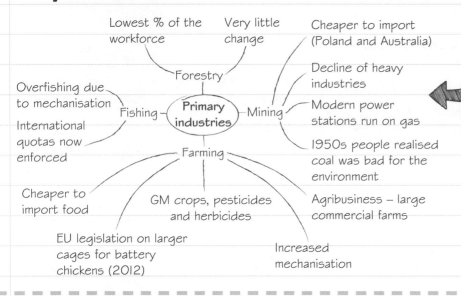

Lowest % of the workforce

Very little change

Cheaper to import (Poland and Australia)

Decline of heavy industries

Modern power stations run on gas

1950s people realised coal was bad for the environment

Agribusiness – large commercial farms

Increased mechanisation

GM crops, pesticides and herbicides

EU legislation on larger cages for battery chickens (2012)

Cheaper to import food

Overfishing due to mechanisation

International quotas now enforced

Forestry

Fishing

Primary industries

Mining

Farming

Many coal mines were closed in the 1970s and 1980s resulting in massive job losses.

## Worked example

**B** HIGHER

Suggest reasons for the decline in the primary sector in the UK. **(4 marks)**

The primary sector (removing raw materials from the ground or sea) has significantly dropped in the UK, with less than 2% of the workforce employed in these industries.

The introduction of mechanisation and machinery has meant there is less need for lots of workers. This has had a particular impact on farming with the introduction of tractors and bailers. Economically it can be much more beneficial to import goods from abroad. Cheap imports from Poland and Australia have resulted in forcing mines to close, and the shift to gas-fired power stations hasn't helped the British coal industry.

### EXAM ALERT!

Try to avoid confusing terminology. Here, focus is on the **primary** sector, so avoid discussing the decline of the manufacturing industry, as this is not relevant.

Students have struggled with exam questions similar to this – **be prepared!**

ResultsPlus

## Now try this

**D-C** FOUNDN

Primary industry in the UK has declined in recent years. Outline **two** reasons for this decline. **(4 marks)**

Remember that there are four main industries that can be described as primary – farming, forestry, fishing and mining. You can discuss any of them.

# Secondary sector decline

Fifty years ago more than 40% of the UK's wealth came from the secondary sector. Now it is estimated that it accounts for only 25% and less than 20% of the workforce are employed in this sector.

## Why the decline?

Cheaper to make products **abroad** (e.g. China) – labour and land are cheaper, regulations are not as demanding

↓

De-industrialisation – loss of traditional industries due to **modern production** and **automation**

↓

**Transport** enables goods to be moved more quickly and efficiently

↓

Modern **communication** networks – easier to keep in touch

↓

Growth of **transnational corporations** (TNCs) – e.g. Coca-Cola, Nike – operate all over the world

↓

**Globalisation** has meant that companies have moved their manufacturing to cheaper locations (often MICs or LICs). This has been helped by increasing **technological advancements** (internet) and the major improvements in **transport** (aircraft and containers, as well as more efficient motorways). For example, Marks and Spencer operates in Portugal, Sri Lanka, Morocco and the Middle East.

## Worked example

**HIGHER B**

Suggest reasons for the decline in the secondary sector in the UK.
**(4 marks)**

The introduction of mechanisation and machinery has meant there is less need for lots of workers. Products are often produced more cheaply abroad and then imported here. A social factor is the perceived idea that factory work is menial. There is a big demand for workers in the tertiary (or service) sector so lots of people are moving to these types of jobs.

The focus of the question is on the **secondary** sector, so avoid discussing primary industries, such as agriculture or fishing.
Remember that the secondary sector is manufacturing industries (making products).

**See also p. 73**

For definitions of economic sectors.

## Now try this

**FOUNDN D-C**

The number of people employed in the secondary sector in the UK has declined.
One reason for this is the growth of transnational corporations (TNCs).

1  What is a TNC? **(1 mark)**
   - ☐ **A** a large company that operates in one country only
   - ☐ **B** a small company that operates all over the world
   - ☐ **C** a small company that operates in one country only
   - ☐ **D** a large company that operates all over the world

2  Give **one** example of a TNC. **(1 mark)**

# China (MIC)

## Industrial explosion

China has recently experienced an industrial explosion and is currently ranked the third most important manufacturing country in the world. Iron and steel, chemicals and fertilisers, shipping, military equipment and space satellites are some of its industries. China is also famous for its consumer products and is globally responsible for:

- 50% clothes and 66% shoes
- 50% microwave ovens
- 33% mobile phones
- 66% photocopiers

**Case study**

You need to know a case study of the growth of the secondary sector in one LIC or MIC.

Available natural resources, e.g. coal, gas, oil to power industries

Cheap workforce earning 40p per hour

Increase in globalisation enables less rich countries to manufacture

Human

Physical

Reasons for growth

Increase in literacy rate – 96% in 2011

Close to other developing countries so good trade routes

Increase in privately owned companies, from 100 in 1979 to 280 000 in 1998

## Positive impacts

✓ 10 fold increase in GNP per capita in the last 20 years

Industrial area in China

## Negative impacts

✗ very little money spent on infrastructure

✗ few laws to protect workers

✗ increase in air, noise and visual pollution

✗ pressure on non-renewable resources due to energy requirements

✗ not addressing regional disparities

## Worked example

Explain **two** impacts that industrialisation can have on a country.

**(4 marks)**

China has experienced growth in its secondary sector industry. The obvious positive impacts are the increase in wealth. GNP per capita has now risen from $816 in 1995 to $5200 in 2011.

Industrialisation can also have negative impacts. Increased manufacturing means more energy is needed and this often comes from non-renewable sources. This has increased air pollution and it is estimated that ¾ of a million Chinese die every year as a result.

You could include positive or negative impacts, or one positive and one negative impact.

## Now try this

Choose either **one LIC or one** MIC that you have studied.

Explain the reasons for the growth in its secondary sector.

**(6 marks)**

# Tertiary sector growth 1

The tertiary (services) sector is considered the most important in HICs and accounts for more than 75% of economic output. Economic improvements and technological advances are major factors in the growth of the tertiary sector.

## Economic improvements

As a country develops and moves along the development pathway people have more **disposable income** to spend on:

- basic items such as food and clothing
- luxury items such as entertainment, holidays, private healthcare and recreation.

11.9 % of the UK population is a member of a health or fitness club.

Because of economic improvements a country is able to afford better **social services**, this means more:

- schools
- medical centres
- hospitals
- libraries.

## Technological advances

It is predicted that by 2015 there will be 7.4 billion mobile devices on the planet.

Increase in IT and telecommunications has led to:

- new job opportunities: internet service providers, website designers, PC and laptop servicing, call centres
- decline in cinemas as it becomes easier to view films at home but an increase in jobs installing, repairing and selling telecommunications equipment.

Between 2006 and 2007 the number of people working in UK call centres increased by 38 000, an increase of more than 6% from the previous year.

## Worked example

**HIGHER B**

Many people have more disposable income.
Outline how this can impact on tertiary industries. **(3 marks)**

In 1995, average disposable income was £12 000, but this increased to £13 500 by 2009. This means that individuals have 'spare money' which can be spent on luxury items such as gym memberships (33% increase in 55-year-olds from 1998 to 2005) and beauty treatments. More disposable income will help service industries grow, as people have the means to pay for them.

There is an excellent use of data in this answer to help support statements. The specific use of examples helps the explanation.

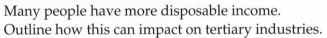

## Now try this

**FOUND'N C**

Explain how improvements in technology have increased the tertiary sector. **(4 marks)**

# Tertiary sector growth 2

## Getting older

Many HICs are becoming **ageing populations**. In the UK 16.5% of the population is over 64 compared to 5% in 1911.

Not all elderly people have a disposable income and often the state pension is inadequate. To provide for these people there has been a growth in charities such as Age UK and a greater demand on Local Authority social service provision.

Many elderly people are able to afford to spend money on shopping and holidays. This is called the **grey pound**. Companies are taking advantage of this, e.g. SAGA holidays, B&Q, L'Oreal, etc.

Holiday companies, charities and shops are all part of the tertiary sector

See also p. 102

For advantages of an ageing population.

## Worked example

HIGHER B-A

Explain how an ageing population can lead to an increase in the tertiary sector. **(4 marks)**

Most HICs such as the UK and Germany are experiencing an ageing population where over 15% of the population are over 64 years of age.

Traditionally older people used to stay at home, but now they are taking advantage of the increased opportunities to shop and travel.

As a result, specialised travel providers such as SAGA have developed, and they tailor their breaks and cruises specifically for people over 50 years. Other companies such as B&Q now sell products aimed at older people (for example, Stannah stairlifts and special garden tools).

Charity shops such as Age UK have increased as not all older people have adequate disposable income – their shops are a good example of a tertiary service.

The student has provided specific details to help answer the question.

Both the reasons supplied have been described and linked to increasing services – the tertiary sector.

## Now try this

FOUNDN D

It is important that you know the **definitions** of key terminology.

Complete the sentences to explain the reasons for the growth of the tertiary sector in the UK.

Use some of the words in the box below. **(5 marks)**

> water  disposable  less  holidays  more  recycled  youthful  manufacturing  farming  ageing

Fewer people are choosing jobs in the primary sector such as _____ because of the long hours and physical activity.

There is an _____ population in the UK.

Many retired people have more _____ income than in the past.

This means that they have _____ money to spend on _____.

# Location of industries 1

A number of factors affect the location of primary, secondary and tertiary activities. These can vary between sectors, but there are some that are common for all three.

## Primary sector

Arable farming is a good example of a primary sector activity. The diagram shows the main environmental and socio-economic factors that make areas of East Anglia in the UK ideal for arable farming.

Relief – flat land for easy crop cultivation

Government – grants and subsidies to help industry

Markets – somewhere to sell the produce

Environment

Labour and Capital – local workforce available, and money for investment

Soil – nutrient-rich, aerated soil for crops to grow

Social  Economic

Climate – adequate sunshine and rainfall

Technology – ease of introducing new machines and farming practices

## Secondary sector

The car industry is an example of a secondary industry.
The Toyota factory at Burnaston, near Derby is a good location because:

👍 there are 100 hectares of flat land available, so factory can expand

👍 there is high local unemployment (with relevant skills) with recent job losses at Rolls-Royce and Brell

👍 it is close to West Midlands, home to many car component companies

👍 it is located on a greenfield site, only 8 km from centre of Derby

👍 it is near attractive villages like Findern popular for homes for managerial workers

👍 there is electricity (energy supply) from local power stations

👍 there are good transport links nearby – A38 and MI

👍 the local county council invested £20 million in the area.

## Worked example

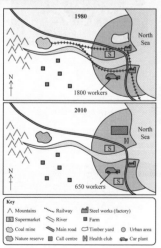

Figure 1

**FOUND'N C**

Study Figure 1, which shows the location of steel works.

Suggest reasons for the location of the steel works. Use evidence from Figure 1 in your answer.   **(3 marks)**

In 1980, the coal mine was very near to the steel works so they had access to coal supplies needed for smelting. The railway enabled goods to be transported as well as helping the coal supplies get to the steel works quickly and easily. The location of the sea enables further transportation and access.

### EXAM ALERT!

When you are asked to use a resource, make sure you do! Aim to include a good range of location factors.

Students have struggled with exam questions similar to this – **be prepared!**

ResultsPlus

## Now try this

**HIGHER B**

Study Figure 1. Outline the reasons for the changes between 1980 and 2010.   **(4 marks)**

# Location of industries 2

## Tertiary sector

The planning process for building the Trafford Shopping Centre, Manchester was one of the longest and most expensive ever in the UK. The centre has 35 million visitors a year and was recently sold for £1650 million.

Before building a shopping centre, planners and developers look at factors such as nearby market, wealth of local people and number of cars per family. This can be mapped using GIS.

Lots of space available to build on.

Excellent transport links, e.g. M6.

Cheaper land prices on the edge of the city – Bid Rent Theory.

Large local market – 10% of the UK's population are within a 45-minute drive.

## Changing places

With the growth of footloose industries (modern industries with relatively free choice of location), location factors are changing.

New and better ICT

Technology like the internet, email and smart phones means customers can shop online and have goods delivered to their homes.

Extensive transport networks

**Modern location factors for tertiary industries**

Motorways, rail and larger ships / aircraft mean industries no longer need to be near sources of raw materials or customers.

Modern industries no longer need local raw materials, like coal and iron ore – most is now imported (such as coal from Australia, Indonesia and Russia).

Raw materials imported

## Worked example

**FOUNDN E**

Many newly built shopping centres are located on the edge of cities. Tick **one** reason why.     **(2 marks)**

☐ **A** limited transport     ☐ **C** land is very expensive

☐ **B** closer to raw materials     ☒ **D** lots of space available to build on

Remember that tertiary industries are footloose and so have free choice over location.

## Now try this

Outline how the factors affecting the location of industry (economic activity) can change over time. You may use examples in your answer.     **(3 marks)**

# Rural de-industrialisation: benefits

De-industrialisation can occur in **rural** (countryside) areas as well as in **urban** areas (towns and cities). There are advantages and disadvantages – benefits and costs – of losing industry in the countryside.

## Old industries

See also p. 82

For more on costs.

200 years ago a number of different industries operated in rural areas, including:

- wool cloth production
- lime making
- breweries
- flour milling
- brick making
- mining for coal, iron, tin, etc.

*An old tin mine in Cornwall*

## Benefits of rural de-industrialisation

- There is less environmental pollution – old slag heaps are landscaped, e.g. Aberfan, South Wales.
- Different industries start to invest – in Consett, NE England, new industry turns over £110 million, 50% more than the original steel plant made.
- Old buildings and land can be made into tourist attractions – the Eden Project, Cornwall is on the site of an old china clay pit.
- Ugly buildings are removed so there is less visual pollution.
- Land can be returned to farmland, called **re-agriculturalisation**.
- **Brownfield** sites can be used for housing and industrial growth – Penallta colliery in Wales was converted into a new village.
- Old industrial land may be used for wildlife, recreation or landfill.

*The Eden Project, Cornwall*

## Worked example

Outline **one** benefit (advantage) of re-industrialisation. **(2 marks)**

One benefit of re-industrialisation is that old, ugly buildings can be knocked down and replaced. New buildings can be used to attract tourists, such as the Eden Project in Cornwall.

Don't just provide a list of advantages. Give one advantage and explain it.

## Now try this

Outline **two** benefits of de-industrialisation in rural areas. Use examples in your answer. **(4 marks)**

81

# Rural de-industrialisation: costs

👎 Jobs are lost in rural areas – closure of the Consett steel plant, NE England in 1980 resulted in 4000 job losses.

👎 The **domino effect** results – less income means less **spending power** which will impact on other economic activities, e.g. tertiary industries such as retail.

👎 There is **less income** from tax because there are no industries to pay tax.

👎 There are increased unemployment benefits to pay.

👎 Rural communities break up as people move to cities (**rural depopulation**), often leaving an ageing population – 20% of Consett's population moved away after the steel works closed.

👎 Derelict buildings look ugly and may encourage vandalism and litter dumping.

Poster protesting at the closure of Consett steel plant

## An expensive business

- Cleaning up the 500 000 viable brownfield sites in the USA would cost an estimated $725 billion.

- It cost €5 million to clean up by-products (sulphuric acid, benzene, ammonium sulphate and tar from exhaust gases) from gas works in Hamburg-Bahrenfeld, near Altona.

- The high concentrations of hydrocarbon waste from mineral oil at the Stülken shipyard in Germany resulted in €9.1 million remediation costs.

- Many contaminated sites now use a process called **solidification** – mixing contaminated material with cement before infilling to help immobilise hazardous contaminates. However, it is very costly at more than $240 per m³!

## Worked example

Complete the sentences to describe the impacts of rural de-industrialisation.

Use some of the words in the box below.

**(5 marks)**

pleasant ~~community~~ rise ~~visual~~ ~~jobs~~ air attractive ~~costs~~ ~~ugly~~ advantages

Rural de-industrialisation can have both _costs_ and benefits. People can lose their _jobs_ and have to move to towns. This can break up the rural _community_ and change the character of an area.

Rural de-industrialisation can have benefits. Disused _ugly_ factories can be demolished, reducing the amount of _visual_ pollution.

> **Read** through the **whole** question first and then **cross through** the answers in the box once you have used the word.

## Now try this

Outline **two** costs of de-industrialisation in rural areas. Use examples in your answer. **(4 marks)**

# Settlement functions

The **function** of a settlement describes what the place did in the past, or still does, often linked to the main economic activity.

## Function types

- **residential** – lots of housing but few services, often **commuter** settlements
- **market town** – centres for trading goods, in accessible areas, at crossroads or near rivers
- **administrative** – focus on the governance of a country or area, often the capital city
- **strategic** – historically providing protection from attack, often on hill tops or inside meander bends

- **industrial** – large proportion of the population working within a certain industry
- **tourism** – rely heavily on the influx of tourists who are attracted by specific characteristics
- **cultural** or **religious**
- **trading**, e.g. a port.

Few settlements now have singular functions. Most large settlements are classified as **multi-functional** (having more than one function).

## Changing functions

Most settlements change their function over time. A good example of this is Benidorm in Spain.

**1** It developed as a defensive function on a hill.

**2** Then into a fishing port as it was situated on the coast.

**3** Agriculture became important when water was transferred from inland.

**4** It became an important tourist destination after roads were built in the area.

## Worked example

**HIGHER C**

Using an example you have studied, describe how a settlement can change its function over time. **(4 marks)**

Benidorm in Spain developed due to its physical location. Being located close to hills enabled the settlement to become a defensive site. It was also near the sea, so its primary function was linked to the fishing industry. When the settlement grew, water was channelled from inland, and supported a growing agricultural function for citrus fruits and olives. However, the development of the main road to Alicante in the 19th century enabled the development of Benidorm as a seaside resort and this has become its main function today.

Writing historically makes it easier to see how the function has changed over time.

## Now try this

**FOUNDN C**

1 What does the term **function** of a settlement mean? **(1 mark)**

2 Look at the map extract of Durham.

What was the original function of Durham? Using map evidence, explain your reasons. **(3 marks)**

# Change in rural communities

There are two main processes causing change in remote rural communities – **depopulation** and **counterurbanisation**.

## Depopulation

Depopulation is the loss of population from an area. It is common in rural areas.

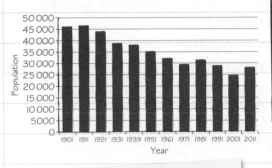

Population change in the Western Isles, Scotland 1901–2011

## Causes of depopulation

- Harsh physical environment (high relief, hard climate).
- Limited job opportunities (fishing, farming).
- 'Bright city lights' draw young people away.
- 18-year-olds go to mainland for further education / university, but few return due to limited job opportunities.

## Impacts of depopulation

- Reduction in pollution from old primary industries means biodiversity can flourish.
- **Services** like shops and schools close down, contributing to the spiral of decline.
- Increased costs per head of public utilities.
- Empty villages and abandoned buildings.
- **Drastically altered population structure**, often leaving an ageing population rather isolated.

## Counterurbanisation

This involves a movement from large cities to smaller ones or from urban to rural areas.

The main reason is that people become discontented with life in the city: the cost of housing, pollution, personal security and quality of life.

On the Isle of Skye, Scotland, 30% of the people are 'outsiders'. The island became more accessible when the Skye Bridge was built, creating a direct link to the mainland.

## Rural population – increase or decrease?

The population of a rural area depends on whether counterurbanisation is greater or smaller than depopulation.

- When counterurbanisation is greater than depopulation – the rural population **increases**.
- When counterurbanisation is less than depopulation – the rural population **decreases**.
- When depopulation equals counterurbanisation – the population is **stable**.

## Worked example

**E**

People leave remote rural areas because

☐ A  some villages are becoming too crowded

☐ B  new roads and houses are being built in cities

☒ C  there is greater choice of facilities in urban areas

☐ D  of a rise in pollution          (1 mark)

## Now try this

Explain **one** social impact of depopulation on remote rural communities. Use an example in your answer.          **(2 marks)**

# Changing urban areas

Urban areas are constantly changing because of the need for more **housing** and the changes that **de-industrialisation** brings.

## Housing

The need for more housing in the UK is due to **social**, **political** and **economic** factors. In 2011, there were 23.4 million households in the UK, and 30% were single person households!

Higher **life** expectancy

Increase in population by 2.1 million 2001–2007

Increase in **personal wealth** – people can afford to live on their own

Low **death rate**

Social

Economic

Ageing population

'New Homes Bonus' schemes for local authorities, worth £431 million in 2012–13

More **households** – more people living alone

Personal **choice**

Political

Environment concerns raise profile of 'eco-housing' – supported by government / local authorities / Eco-Development group

More **divorces**

New **economic policies** – 'Get Britain Building Fund' (Nov 2011) to encourage development of new homes

Later **marriages**

## De-industrialisation

The reduction of industry is usually the result of social and economic change.

Much of the heavy industry that existed in the UK (e.g. shipping, iron and steel) has closed down and many manufacturing industries have relocated abroad, usually to Asia where production is cheaper. Also, there has been a shift from secondary industries (manufacturing) to tertiary (services).

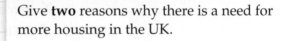

## Worked example

Give **two** reasons why there is a need for more housing in the UK. **(4 marks)**

Population has increased from 59 million in 2001 to 60 million in 2007. Increased population means more homes are needed. Lots more families are splitting up and there is more divorce so two homes are needed. This means more homes generally.

To develop your answer, you need to elaborate on each point you make. Include relevant data or statistics if you can.

## Now try this

Many small flats are being built as a response to changes in the population structure of the UK. Describe these changes in the population structure. **(4 marks)**

# Land use change 1

An estimated 3 million new homes will be needed by 2020. We can build them on **greenfield** or **brownfield** land, in **urban fringes** or **commuter belts**.

## Urban fringe housing estates

### Advantages and disadvantages

✓ Relatively close to the city centre.

✓ Popular for offices and factories, so many job opportunities.

✓ Space for large leisure and shopping complexes.

✗ Built on greenfield* land so countryside is lost to development.

✗ Increases urban sprawl.

✗ Have similar architecture and layout with the same socio-economic groups.

> *Greenfield – land that has not been used or built on before, often in **rural** areas, that is being considered for development.

## Eco-towns

Developers are now considering the idea of eco-towns.

Ten out of these 15 proposed sites will be chosen to be eco-towns

## Eco-friendly?

There are pros and cons to eco-towns.

✓ They can provide up to 20000 new homes.

✓ Housing can be allocated to people with lower incomes – 30% in largest eco-town.

✓ They are largely car-free.

✓ They can be made more **sustainable** by reducing carbon emissions and using recycled materials.

✗ Increases urban sprawl.

✗ Built on greenfield land.

✗ Very little provision for employment.

## Worked example

**FOUNDN F-E**

Look at this list of advantages and disadvantages of developing land on greenfield sites.

**Two** of these factors are **advantages**.
Put a cross in the **two** correct boxes.  (2 marks)

☐ A  no electricity or water supply

☐ B  green spaces are lost

☒ C  attractive surroundings

☐ D  buildings could disturb wildlife

☐ E  high level of noise during development

☒ F  cheaper land than in the city centre

## Now try this

**FOUNDN E**

State **one** advantage and **one** disadvantage of building in the urban fringe.  (2 marks)

### EXAM ALERT!

Make sure you read these questions carefully as they often catch students out. Try putting a 'D' next to each disadvantage and an 'A' next to each advantage.

Students have struggled with exam questions similar to this – **be prepared!**  ResultsPlus

# Land use change 2

## Redeveloping the inner city

- This uses **brownfield\*** sites.
- Houses are more centrally located within the city.
- A wide variety of shops and entertainment is available.
- The need to build new roads and provide services (water, gas and electricity) is reduced.
- There are issues over personal security. Developers are now looking into building **gated communities**.

> \***Brownfield** – a piece of land that has been previously developed and is now **abandoned**. These areas are waiting to be redeveloped.

### NIMBY

Remember that development on any type of land (greenfield or brownfield) is often subject to **opposition**. Individuals, businesses and organisations will have different viewpoints. Remember the acronym NIMBY – **N**ot **i**n **m**y **b**ack **y**ard!

### Gated communities

High gates with restricted access, CCTV and security guards are becoming common. However, houses in gated communities are very expensive so they may only be an option for more affluent people.

## Worked example

Derelict buildings on brownfield sites are being demolished and replaced by blocks of small flats.

1  What is the term used to describe this process?  **(1 mark)**

   Redevelopment

2  Explain **one** advantage of developing the rural-urban fringe.  **(3 marks)**

   One advantage of developing in the rural–urban fringe is that it is located close to the city centre. This may encourage the relocation of new offices and factories, which will increase job opportunities for local people.

### EXAM ALERT!

Make sure you learn your terminology. Few students give the correct term for when houses are built on brownfield sites. Remember – **redevelopment**!

Students have struggled with exam questions similar to this – **be prepared!**

ResultsPlus

## Now try this

Explain the advantages of developing the inner city.  **(4 marks)**

# De-industrialisation

De-industrialisation results in large areas of derelict land and unused buildings. Cities with derelict industrial areas face the challenge of the two 'R's:

- **renewal** to provide economic activities and employment after de-industrialisation
- **redevelopment** to create new uses for old buildings or to clear them away and rebuild.

## Bradford, West Yorkshire

Bradford developed as a result of the wool / textile industry, but the second half of the 20th century saw industrial decline.

### Success!
Bradford Council has had great success enforcing the two 'R's, by:

**Renewal**
- attracting modern industries like engineering and ICT to the area
- providing new tourism and leisure facilities.

**Redevelopment**
- rejuvenating old mills, converting them into museums, craft centres, galleries and small flats
- demolishing old buildings to make **brownfield** land available for development.

Old mill converted into residential units

## Vaux, Sunderland

The 13 hectare site of the former Vaux brewery which closed in 1999 is one of the most significant brownfield sites in NE England.

New **offices** and **shops**

New **hotel** — **Renewal plan** — 3000 new **jobs**

1000 new **homes** — **Green space** by river

Sunderland Arc's renewal plan for the site

---

## Worked example

Look at the photograph. It shows an area of urban renewal.

Look at the **evidence** in photographs to help you answer these questions.

1 What is the land use of this area now? **(1 mark)**

☒ A housing     ☐ C sports hall
☐ B factory     ☐ D shopping mall

2 This site has been built on before. It can be described as a: **(1 mark)**

☐ A greenfield site     ☒ C brownfield site
☐ B rural site     ☐ D derelict site

---

## Now try this

Explain the consequences (impacts) of de-industrialisation in the UK. Use examples in your answer. **(6 marks)**

# Brownfield and greenfield sites

With any new development – housing, recreational or industrial – a choice needs to be made whether to build on **brownfield** or **greenfield**.

See also p. 86 and p. 87

For definition of greenfield and brownfield.

## Brown or green?

Any developer knows that there are **advantages** and **disadvantages** to both brownfield sites and greenfield sites. The location of residential areas is relatively flexible. However, retail, service and manufacturing companies will be a little choosier about where they locate.

### Brownfield land

👍 helps **rejuvenate** old or disused areas

👍 reduces loss of countryside and helps hold onto farmland

👍 services (water, gas, sewage and electricity) already in place

👍 often near areas of employment, reducing the need to **commute**

👎 some sites (particularly industrial) are contaminated with pollutants – Stülken shipyard, Germany cost €9.1 million to clean before it could be redeveloped

👎 old buildings may need to be demolished

👎 surrounding areas may be run down – hard to attract investors

👎 may lack modern transport infrastructure, so cost more to develop.

### Greenfield land

👍 relatively cheap to develop

👍 new houses quicker to build

👍 layout not hampered by previous development

👍 often located in 'healthier' areas

👎 valuable farmland lost

👎 wildlife habitats disturbed, with possible reduction in biodiversity

👎 increased noise and light **pollution** plus visual pollution from loss of rural scenery

👎 recreational land lost – could encourage urban sprawl.

## Worked example (HIGHER B)

Explain the advantages of developing brownfield sites **(3 marks)**

Brownfield sites already have electricity, water supplies and transport, so there is no need to build these. Builders will therefore save money. Using brownfield land means you are not using greenfield. This will help save the countryside and protect wildlife habitats.

Make sure that you focus on the correct type of land to be developed – **brownfield**.

## Now try this (FOUNDN E-D)

Complete the sentences to describe the advantages of redeveloping brownfield sites for new housing. Use some of the words in the box below. **(5 marks)**

reduces   electricity   difficult   increases
employment   easier   saves   invests

Brownfield sites already have existing supplies of water and _____. This means that the developer _____ money. Brownfield sites are often near areas of _____, making it _____ to travel to work. Developing brownfield sites also _____ the amount of countryside needed for new housing.

# Growing cities in LICs

Urban areas in LICs are growing much faster than in HICs.

## Exploding cities

This rapid population growth could be termed an **urban explosion**.

It is estimated that 40% of all urban growth in LICs is a result of **rural** to **urban migration**, and 60% is a result of high **natural increase**.

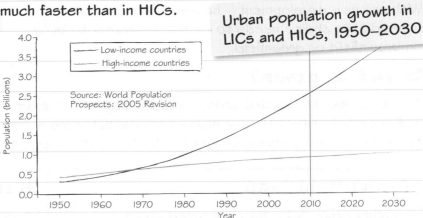

Urban population growth in LICs and HICs, 1950–2030

Source: World Population Prospects: 2005 Revision

## Reasons for growth

 **Rural to urban migration**

There are **rural push factors** (factors that 'force' you to leave an area) and **urban pull factors** (factors that 'encourage' you to move).

**Push factors**
- lack of employment
- mechanisation of farming
- lack of government support
- lack of investment
- limited schooling

**Pull factors**
- employment opportunities, higher wages
- pace and excitement of urban life
- access to public utilities like piped water, sewage and electricity
- government support

 **Natural increase**

**Increase in birth rate (BR)**
- high percentage of population of child-bearing age leads to high **fertility rate**
- lack of **contraception** or **education** about family planning

**Lower death rate (DR)**
- improved medical facilities helps lower **infant mortality rate** (IMR)
- higher **life expectancy** (LE) due to better living conditions and diet

**Natural increase** is the rise in population caused by the birth rate exceeding the death rate.

**Fertility rate** is the number of live births per 1000 women of child-bearing age (15–44).

## Worked example

Suggest reasons for the rapid growth of urban areas in LICs. **(3 marks)**

In rural areas there is limited work which is often related to farming and is often low paid. This has meant that the possibility of better jobs and housing in the urban areas has 'pulled' people towards the cities. Also LICs have higher birth rates (limited contraception and medical care) so more people are being born which also increases the urban population.

Make sure you include a reference to natural increase.

## Now try this

Outline **two** impacts that migration can have on urban areas in LICs.

**(4 marks)**

# Dhaka

Dhaka is the capital city of Bangladesh, Asia. It is one of the poorest countries in the world. Its population is estimated to be 12 million, but is expected to increase to 21 million by 2025.

**Case study**

You need to know a case study of the effects of rapid growth in an LIC.

## Growing pressure on housing

**Diseases** occur because of the overcrowding and poor conditions, e.g. diarrhoea, tuberculosis, measles, malaria and dengue fever.

**Air pollution** is bad because of domestic fires, factories and exhaust fumes making the density of air-borne particles five times higher than acceptable levels.

Rural–urban migration has led to rapid increase in population of the city. A lack of homes has resulted in the building of **shanty towns** (botis).

**Waste** builds up because there is no provision to get rid of it, this causes health hazards.

Water is **polluted** as a result of contamination from industry.

The UN predicts that by 2050 Dhaka will have a population of 40 million.

---

**Worked example**

Describe the conditions that people often find themselves in as a result of rapid urban growth in an LIC. **(4 marks)**

Dhaka in Bangladesh has a massive urban population that is fuelled by rural–urban migration and the effects of a high BR and decreasing DR, leading to a high rate of natural increase.

The government cannot afford to house the thousands of people coming in, and so they often end up in makeshift housing called botis – these are slum areas.

They often lack access to proper services such as clean water and electricity and as a result disease is prevalent (particularly typhoid and cholera). There is massive overcrowding which leads to issues over disposal of sewage and water pollution.

This is a clearly written answer which includes some good references to the impacts on housing. This is then linked to how it affects the standard of living.

The use of an example is good; however the question has not stipulated the use of case study specific detail.

Try to make links between the different impacts.

---

**Now try this**

Choose an urban area in an LIC that you have studied. Explain the effects of rapid urban growth. **(4 marks)**

You need to link this to a **specific** example you have studied. Common examples are Dhaka, Bangladesh and Cairo, Egypt.

# World population

Since 1950, the population of the world has grown quickly. This has been termed the **population explosion**.

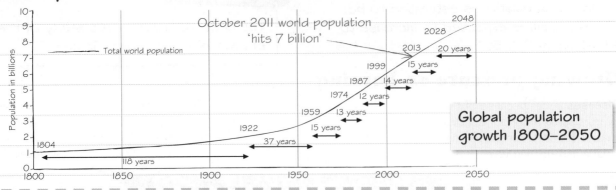

Global population growth 1800–2050

## Population distribution

Population density is the measure of the number of people per km². Global population is not distributed evenly. Some areas are **densely** populated (many people) while others are **sparsely** populated (few people). Population distribution evolves over centuries. It is affected by three main factors: **physical**, **human** and **historical**.

Very cold (down to −7°C), soil often frozen (permafrost) hard to grow crops – sparsely populated

Good water supply, low-lying land, fertile soil for crops, many natural resources and good communication and stable governments – densely populated

Too hot (av. 27° C) and wet (av. >2000 mm/year), thick forest hard for people and communications – sparsely populated

Low-lying land, good rainfall, fertile soils for crops, four growing seasons, good trade access – densely populated

Too hot (av. 55°C) and low rainfall (av. 76 mm/year) hard for crops and people – sparsely populated

• 100 000 people

**Physical and human factors**

Cities like London and Rome have grown in population because they are significant financial and cultural capitals

**Historical factors**

## Worked example

FOUNDN C

Suggest **two** human factors why areas like the one shown in the photo are sparsely populated. **(2 marks)**

West Wales is sparsely populated. A possible reason for the pattern could be the lack of roads, which would make transport more difficult. Another reason could be the lack of services such as shops, which would make it difficult to get food and supplies.

## Now try this

HIGHER B

Explain the reasons why the population of the world is not evenly distributed. Use examples in your answer. **(4 marks)**

# The demographic transition model

The population of a country depends on certain **variables** which can change over time. These changes can be seen on the **demographic transition model** (DTM).

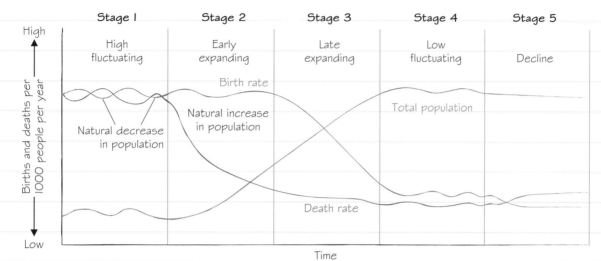

Population change is affected by:

**1** **birth rate** – the number of live births per thousand per year

**2** **death rate** – the number of deaths per thousand per year

**3** **migration** – the movement of people in (immigrants) and out (emigrants) of a country.

When birth rate and / or immigration is greater than death rate and / or emigration, the population **increases**.

When death rate and / or emigration is greater than birth rate and / or immigration, the population **decreases**.

When birth rate and / or immigration is equal to death rate and / or emigration, the population **is stable**.

## Worked example

Remember that the term **fluctuate** means it goes up and down!

Figure 1

Study Figure 1, a diagram of the DTM.

1 In which stage of the model does the death rate fluctuate? **(1 mark)**

☒ Stage 1    ☐ Stage 3
☐ Stage 2    ☐ Stage 4

2 In which stage of the model is population growth greatest? **(1 mark)**

☐ Stage 1    ☐ Stage 3
☒ Stage 2    ☐ Stage 4

## Now try this

Describe what happens to the population growth rate in Stage 3 of the DTM. **(3 marks)**

Think about the birth and death rates as well as the natural change.

93

# Birth and death rates

## Reasons for changes

As a country becomes more developed, its birth and death rates can decrease. The reasons for this can be social, medical, economic and political. The diagram below shows the affect of these factors at the five different stages of the development transition model.

| Birth rates | | | |
| --- | --- | --- | --- |
| Stage 1 and 2 (high) | Stage 3 (decreasing) | Stage 4 (low) | Stage 5 (low) |
| Little or no contraception (● ●) | Widespread birth control (● ● ● ●) | Birth control (● ● ●) | |
| Children are seen as assets (●) | Smaller families preferred (● ●) | Working women delaying the age to start having a family (●) | |
| Children are seen as status symbols (●) | Government policies introduced e.g. China (●) | Pensions readily available (● ● ●) | |
| Children needed to look after elderly (● ●) | Expense of bringing up children (●) | Grey population reliant on smaller group of working population due to lower birth rates (● ●) | |

| Death rates | | |
| --- | --- | --- |
| Stage 1 (high) | Stage 2 and 3 (decreasing) | Stage 4 and 5 (low) |
| Infant mortality rate is high (●) | Infant mortality rate is lower (●) | Medical care is good (● ●) |
| High incidences of disease (●) | Improved health care and hygiene (● ●) | Old people's homes and geriatric care is readily available (● ●) |
| Poor housing and hygiene (● ●) | Safer water and better waste disposal (● ● ●) | Pensions available to support people in old age (●) |
| Little or no health care (● ●) | | Key  ● Social   ● Economic<br>● Medical   ● Political |

**Limitations** to the demographic transition model.
- It is a generalisation and not all countries will follow each and every stage.
- Countries go through the model at different speeds, according to how fast they develop.

## Worked example

HIGHER **C**

Suggest reasons why birth rates are low during Stage 3 of the demographic transition model. **(4 marks)**

Birth rates are low in Stage 3 because there have been advances in paediatric medicine and babies are now receiving jabs for childhood diseases (TB and polio). This means that they are surviving so the infant mortality rate drops, and parents do not need to have more children.

Contraception has also become widely accepted which reduces the birth rate. In HICs women are becoming more career minded and so do not want to have so many children, therefore birth rates also drop.

In this answer a range of reasons has been suggested and each one has been linked to why it impacts on the birth rate.

## Now try this

FOUND<sup></sup> **C**

Explain why the death rate is decreasing in Stage 2 of the demographic transition model. **(4 marks)**

### EXAM ALERT!

Try to elaborate on your ideas using the resource and avoid just stating simple points.

Students have struggled with exam questions similar to this – **be prepared!**

ResultsPlus

# Population in China

The population distribution of China is **uneven**.

Some areas are **densely** populated while other areas are **sparsely** populated.

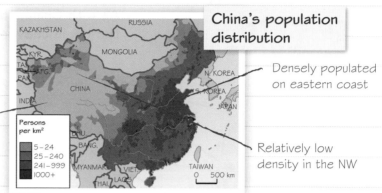

China's population distribution

Densely populated on eastern coast

Sparsely populated in the west

Relatively low density in the NW

Persons per km²
- 5-24
- 25-240
- 241-999
- 1000+

0    500 km

There are **human** and **physical** factors that account for the differences in population densities.

## Human factors

**1** **Economic growth** – Heavy investment in the 1990s drove industrial growth in the E and SE – textiles, plastics and wood products. Development of local ports encouraged the economic boom.

**2** **Communications** – Growth of industry created transport networks. Ports such as Qingdao and Hong Kong encouraged high population densities due to employment.

## Physical factors

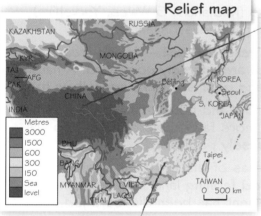

Relief map

Metres
- 3000
- 1500
- 600
- 300
- 150
- Sea level

0    500 km

Mountainous areas make it hard to grow crops, so population is less dense (Tibet)

Lower rainfall (west) leads to drought conditions and less water for people and farming

Flatter land enables cities to expand (e.g. Shanghai)

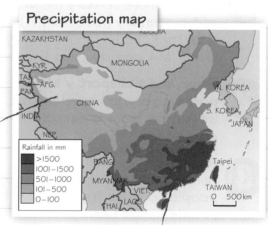

Precipitation map

Rainfall in mm
- >1500
- 1001-1500
- 501-1000
- 101-500
- 0-100

0    500 km

High rainfall (east coast) benefits farming and provides water for the population

## Worked example

Look at the choropleth map of China above, which shows population distribution. Describe the distribution of population. Use evidence from the map in your answer.

**(3 marks)**

It is densely populated (more than 200 people per km²) on the east and south coasts of China. It is sparsely populated in the west (less than 10 people per km²), and has a relatively low population in the north-west.

## Now try this

Explain why some parts of eastern China are densely populated.

**(4 marks)**

# Population in the UK

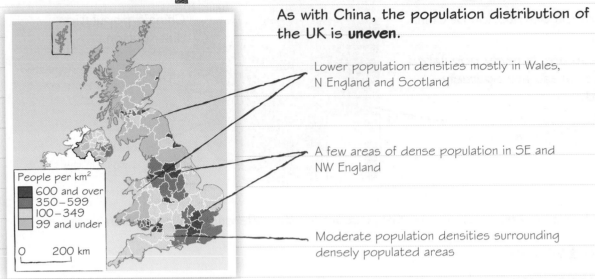

As with China, the population distribution of the UK is **uneven**.

Lower population densities mostly in Wales, N England and Scotland

A few areas of dense population in SE and NW England

Moderate population densities surrounding densely populated areas

People per km²
- 600 and over
- 350–599
- 100–349
- 99 and under

0    200 km

---

There are **human** and **physical** factors that account for these differences in population densities.

## Human Factors

**1** **Employment** – As the UK moves towards more tertiary (services) and quaternary (research, IT) industries, people move to key areas (M4 corridor, and London).

**2** **Trade and transport** – Major ports (Liverpool) need a large workforce, so are densely populated.

**3** **Accessibility** – Being near railways and major roads allows people to move freely, so people settle nearby.

## Physical Factors

**1** **Resources** – Apart from London, the highest population densities are near coalfields (Midlands, S Wales, Yorkshire), even after deindustrialisation.

**2** **Climate, relief and soil** – Upland areas (e.g. Scotland) are **sparsely** populated. A harsh climate and poor soil make agriculture hard.

**3** The SE, SW and E have flatter land, richer soil and more favourable climates, so are more **densely** populated.

**4** Some areas of the UK (East Anglia) have such good farming land that settlement development has been discouraged.

---

## Worked example

**HIGHER B**

Explain **two** reasons why some areas of the UK are densely populated. Use an example in your answer. **(4 marks)**

South Wales is densely populated due primarily to the development of traditional industries such as iron and steel, as well as being located close to main ports such as Cardiff. This required a large workforce and so encouraged dense populations. South Wales is also easily accessible via the M4 motorway to London so enables people to travel from South Wales to other areas.

Make sure you know **one** area of the UK that is densely populated and one that is sparsely populated. You should also know the reasons why.

---

## Now try this

**FOUND'N D-C**

Look at the population density map of the UK above. Describe the distribution of the population within the UK. **(3 marks)**

# Coping with overpopulation

## China

Countries that are overpopulated experience many problems, such as overcrowding, shortages of food, etc. Faced with a huge population growth, the Chinese government introduced schemes in 1980 to reduce the birth rate.

**Case study**

You need to know how two contrasting countries cope with population problems.

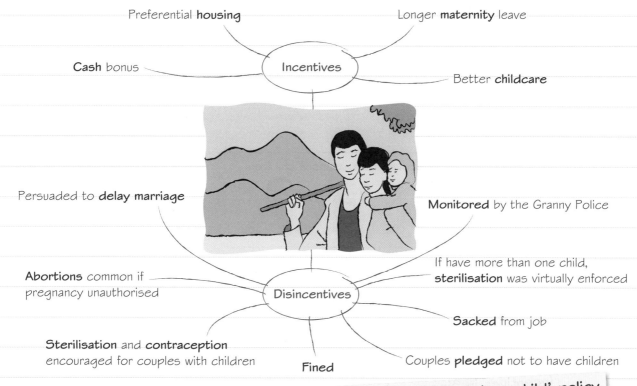

Preferential **housing**

Longer **maternity** leave

**Cash** bonus

Incentives

Better **childcare**

Persuaded to **delay marriage**

**Monitored** by the Granny Police

**Abortions** common if pregnancy unauthorised

Disincentives

If have more than one child, **sterilisation** was virtually enforced

**Sacked** from job

**Sterilisation** and **contraception** encouraged for couples with children

**Fined**

Couples **pledged** not to have children

Aspects of China's 'one child' policy

The policy was relaxed in rural areas in 1996 to allow couples to have more than one child. Overall, the scheme has been very successful – the birth rate in China has dropped from 34 per 1000 in 1970 to 13 per 1000 in 2008.

---

## Worked example

 **FOUND'N D**

Give **one** incentive and **one** disincentive used by a country to reduce its birth rate. **(2 marks)**

Incentive – Longer maternity leave for women

Disincentive – Fined or sacked from job

You need to give **examples** of both an incentive and a disincentive for a country that is overpopulated.

## Now try this

 **HIGHER A**

Explain the incentives and disincentives used by a country trying to decrease the birth rate. **(6 marks)**

**EXAM ALERT!**

When answering higher mark questions make sure your answer is well organised and aim to include relevant examples to support your points.

Students have struggled with exam questions similar to this – **be prepared!** ResultsPlus

# Coping with underpopulation

## Singapore

**Case study**

You need to know how two contrasting countries cope with population problems.

Countries that are underpopulated experience many problems, such as too few workers to support its ageing population. During the 1960s the Singapore government was worried that it would become overpopulated, and worked hard to reduce the birth rate. The policy was so successful that in the mid-1980s the government had to reverse the policy, introducing a 'Have 3 or more – if you can afford' policy.

Government matched couples' savings in Child Development Accounts

Preferential access to best **schools**

Only graduate immigrants encouraged to settle to help raise birth rate

**Incentives to have more children**

Cheaper nurseries

Spacious apartments

$3000 for 1st and 2nd child, $6000 for 3rd and 4th

Non-residents subject to 'Stop at 2' policy

Counselling discouraged women from abortions or sterilisation after 2nd child

Incentives in Singapore's '3 or more' policy

**See also p. 102**  For details on how underpopulation can lead to an ageing population.

## Worked example

**C** FOUND'N

Choose a country that is trying to increase its birth rate. Outline two methods used by this country to increase its birth rate.    **(4 marks)**

Singapore is trying to increase its birth rate. It has done this by giving $3000 for the 1st and 2nd child. If couples have a 3rd or 4th child, they receive $6000. The government has also introduced the CDA – child development account. This is a savings account where the government matches the savings put in by the parents.

## EXAM ALERT!

Read questions carefully. Some students make the mistake of talking about China and its 'one child' policy when answering this question.

Students have struggled with exam questions similar to this – **be prepared!**

## Now try this

**C-B** HIGHER

Describe how **one** country has tried to increase its birth rate.    **(3 marks)**

# Population pyramids: LICs

Age and gender are important population characteristics. These can be shown for a country in a graphic form called a **population pyramid**. Population pyramids differ for countries at different levels of development.

## Typical LIC 'pop pyramid'

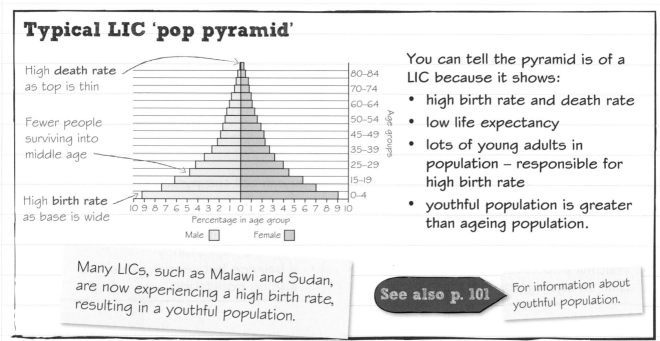

High **death rate** as top is thin

Fewer people surviving into middle age

High **birth rate** as base is wide

Percentage in age group

Male ☐    Female ☐

You can tell the pyramid is of a LIC because it shows:

- high birth rate and death rate
- low life expectancy
- lots of young adults in population – responsible for high birth rate
- youthful population is greater than ageing population.

Many LICs, such as Malawi and Sudan, are now experiencing a high birth rate, resulting in a youthful population.

See also p. 101 For information about youthful population.

---

## Worked example

**HIGHER C**

Study Figure 1. It shows a population pyramid for a country.

Pyramid A

MALE      Age      FEMALE

Population (in millions)

Figure 1

Complete pyramid A. Use the data in the table below. **(1 mark)**

| Age | Female |
|-----|--------|
| 30–39 | 2.2 million |
| 60–69 | 1.4 million |

Use a **ruler** and a **sharp pencil** when completing the pyramid.

---

## Now try this

**FOUNDN D**

Study the pyramid below

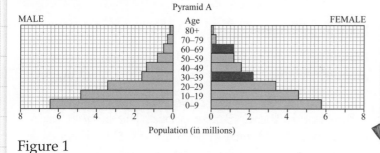

Female ☐
Male ☐

Age groups

Percentage in age group

1. Which level of development best describes the pyramid? **(1 mark)**
2. Give a reason for your answer to question 1. **(1 mark)**

# Population pyramids: MICs and HICs

## Typical MIC pyramid

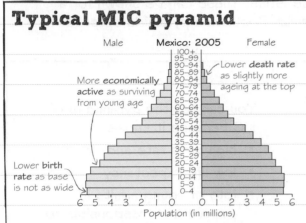

Male    Mexico: 2005    Female

More **economically active** as surviving from young age

Lower **death rate** as slightly more ageing at the top

Lower **birth rate** as base is not as wide

Population (in millions)

You can tell the pyramid is of a MIC because it shows:
- lower birth and death rates
- higher life expectancy
- a more economically active people
- youthful population generally greater than an ageing population.

## Typical HIC pyramid

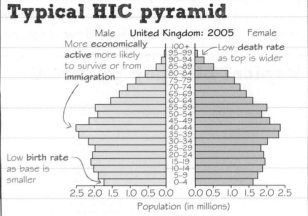

Male    United Kingdom: 2005    Female

More **economically active** more likely to survive or from immigration

Low **death rate** as top is wider

Low **birth rate** as base is smaller

Population (in millions)

You can tell the pyramid is of a HIC because it shows:
- low birth and death rates
- a more economically active population
- high life expectancy
- a balance between youthful and ageing population.

See also p. 101
For information about ageing population.

Many HICs, such as Germany and Italy, are now experiencing a very low birth rate, resulting in an **ageing population**.

## Worked example

HIGHER B

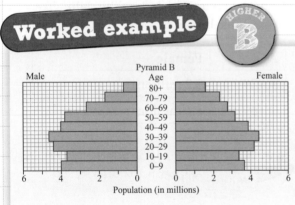

Pyramid B

Male    Age    Female

80+
70–79
60–69
50–59
40–49
30–39
20–29
10–19
0–9

Population (in millions)

Look at pyramid B.

Describe the shape of pyramid B. Use data in your answer. **(3 marks)**

The pyramid has a wide base with approximately 7.8 million in the 0–9 age group. The largest age group is 30–39 with approximately 9.1 million of the population. The top of the pyramid is quite wide with nearly 2 million 80+. This pyramid looks like that of an HIC.

## Now try this

FOUND<sup>N</sup> D

Complete the sentences which outline the features of the population pyramid of a typical HIC. Use some of the words in the box below. **(5 marks)**

low  working  death  narrow  top  high  base  birth  wider  expectancy

The _____ of the pyramid will be small as the birth rate is _____.
The top of the pyramid will be _____. This means the _____ rate is low. This means that the life _____ will be quite high.

# Young and old

## The issue

Few countries have a balanced population. Generally a country will either have a youthful population (lots of people under 16 years) or an ageing population (lots of elderly 65+).

- **Youthful** populations tend to occur in countries that have high birth and death rates (LICs such as Malawi and Sudan).

- **Ageing** populations tend to occur in countries that have low birth and death rates (HICs such as Japan and Germany).

Having a youthful population and having an ageing population each bring their own challenges.

## The challenges

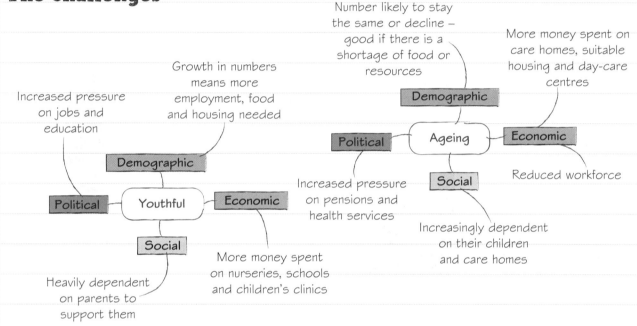

- Increased pressure on jobs and education
- Growth in numbers means more employment, food and housing needed

**Demographic**

**Political** — Youthful — **Economic**

**Social**

- Heavily dependent on parents to support them
- More money spent on nurseries, schools and children's clinics

- Number likely to stay the same or decline – good if there is a shortage of food or resources
- More money spent on care homes, suitable housing and day-care centres

**Demographic**

**Political** — Ageing — **Economic**

**Social**

- Increased pressure on pensions and health services
- Reduced workforce
- Increasingly dependent on their children and care homes

## Worked example

Describe the consequences of an ageing population. **(3 marks)**

One of the problems that will occur is the need for more nursing homes to look after the elderly people. This could mean that money will need to be cut from youth education. It could also mean that the workforce is reduced because there may not be enough young people to work.

## EXAM ALERT!

Students usually answer this question well, commenting on pensions and the idea that we may have to work for longer. Some mistakenly talk about an increase in unemployment instead of a reduction in the workforce.

Students have struggled with exam questions similar to this – **be prepared!** ResultsPlus

## Now try this

Outline the consequences (impacts) of a youthful population. **(2 marks)**

You can take this question from either a positive or negative viewpoint.

# An ageing population

Many HICs are now experiencing an ageing population. There are advantages and disadvantages to this population structure. You will need to know what these are for a specific country.

Many HICs (UK, Germany, Japan) do not have enough babies being born to replace those people that die. The population is becoming **greyer** and this is likely to increase in the future.

**Case study**

You need to know a case study of the advantages and disadvantages of an ageing population.

## The UK

- In 2008, there were 10 million people aged 65 and over.
- Within the next 20 years, this figure is predicted to increase to nearly 16 million.
- By 2050, the number aged 65 and over is likely to be 19 million – 25% of the UK's total population.
- By 2050, 8 million people will be 80 and over.

### Positive impacts

Good health, paid-up mortgages, empty 'nests' and lots of disposable income for the elderly mean:

👍 **disposable income** welcomed by UK retailers

👍 growth in overseas spending **SKI** (Spending Kids' Inheritance) – LIC destinations attractive

👍 more **grey ghettos** (retirement resorts) equipped for providing for social and medical needs of elderly.

### Negative impacts

👎 There are fewer people in the workforce, so less tax to help pay for pensions.

👎 Many elderly now live in care homes rather than being looked after by their children.

👎 The present state pension is inadequate and needs to be raised.

👎 There is deprivation for many pensioners, with issues over funding for extra social services.

---

**Worked example**   HIGHER C

Describe the consequences (impacts) of an ageing population.

**(3 marks)**

With an ageing population there is a decreased workforce, which could impact on industry. This would put pressure on governments to pay for more state pensions to more elderly, so they may have to increase taxes. More old people would require an increase in medical care so more care homes and facilities will be required. Suitable housing for the elderly with relevant mobility devices such as stairlifts will also need to be built.

The question has not asked you for an example, but questions such as these become easier to answer when you apply it to a case study and give examples.

Common examples are the UK and Japan.

---

**Now try this**   FOUND'N C

Choose one country with an ageing population. Suggest the advantages of an ageing population for this country.

**(4 marks)**

# People on the move

Modern transport means that people can now move about more easily and quickly than in the past.

## Short-term, long-term

There are different types of **migration**.

**1**   **Short-term migration** lasts a **short** time and the location is often **temporary**, e.g. foreign worker with a six-month contract.

**2**   **Long-term migration** lasts **longer** than short time. The location can be **temporary** or **permanent**.

> **Migration** means a movement that involves a change of home.
> The location and length of time are determined by the reason for the migration.

## Net migration

People coming into a country are **immigrants**. People leaving are **emigrants**.

- When the number of immigrants is greater than the number of emigrants, you have **net in-migration**.
- When the number of emigrants is greater than the number of immigrants, you have **net out-migration**.
- When the number of immigrants and emigrants is equal, you have a **migration balance**.

> There are many forms of migration:
> - national – within a country
> - international – between countries
> - rural to urban
> - urban to rural.

## Forced and voluntary migration

Migration can be forced or voluntary.

**1**   **Forced migration** is when people have no choice but to move. Reasons might include:

- religious or political persecution, e.g. Tutsi and Hutu in Rwanda
- invasion e.g. Tibetans escaping invading Chinese troops
- natural hazards, e.g. earthquakes, volcanoes and hurricanes.

**2**   **Voluntary migration** is when people choose to move. Reasons might include:

- moving for a better job or pay
- to be close to family
- to live in a more attractive area.

> Forced migration can result in refugees. Once the threat is removed, refugees often return.

## Worked example

FOUNDⁿ
**F-E**

> Hi – my name is Kaspars!
>
> I have chosen to migrate from my village in Latvia where health care is poor. After leaving business school in Latvia, I wanted a job that would pay higher wages.
>
> I am now living with my wife and daughter in the UK where there are more job opportunities and a choice of good schools for my daughter.
>
> Figure 1

Look at the following types of population movement. Choose the **two** items that best describe the population movement in Figure 1 by putting crosses in two of the boxes below. **(2 marks)**

| | | | | |
|---|---|---|---|---|
| ☒ | **A** international | | ☐ | **D** national |
| ☐ | **B** forced | | ☒ | **E** voluntary |
| ☐ | **C** short-term | | ☐ | **F** retirement |

> The question has asked you to choose more than one item. Look out for anything in bold in the question, like the word **two**.

## Now try this

HIGHER
**C**

Some migrants can be described as refugees. What is meant by the term 'refugee'? **(2 marks)**

# Migration into and within Europe

After the Second World War there were large flows of migrants into and within Europe.

## To the UK

Migration to the UK was actively encouraged by the UK government during the 1950s and 1960s, allowing free entry for Commonwealth citizens, e.g. Caribbean, India, Pakistan and Bangladesh. Migrants moved to find jobs so were **economic migrants**.

- By 1971 there were over 1 million immigrants from Commonwealth countries.
- Migrants found jobs in the textile and steel industry, public transport or opened corner shops or restaurants.
- By the 1970s controls were put in place to reduce migration because there were enough workers.

## Within Europe

Migration within Europe occurred in:

1945 – people fleeing communism, e.g. Polish, Ukranians and Hungarians (**forced migration**)

1991 – collapse of Soviet Union meant people could travel more freely, e.g. German reunification

1993 – border controls relaxed within European Union (economic migrants)

2004 – access for Eastern Europeans

## Patterns of migration in Europe

Small net migration gain because most migrants only stay for a year so are considered short-term migrants.

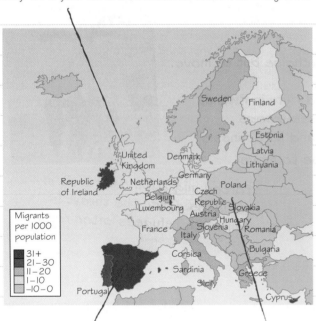

Net migration gain because of arrival of illegal migrants from Africa and because of people retiring there to the Sun.

Net migration loss because people from new member countries of the EU, e.g. Poland and Slovakia, have moved to other countries for jobs and pay.

## Illegal migration

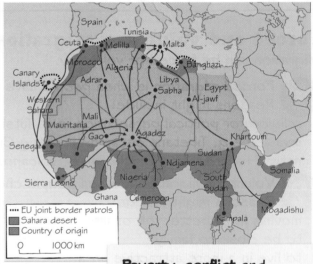

Poverty, **conflict** and **civil war** have forced people to arrive illegally in Europe from African countries. They are smuggled into Europe often via Malta or the Canary Islands.

## Worked example

Some immigrants who come to the UK are refugees.
**What is meant by the term refugee? (1 mark)**
A refugee is a person who has been forced to flee an area to take refuge elsewhere.

It is important that you learn the definitions of key terminology.

## Now try this

What is an **economic migrant**?
**(1 mark)**

# Impacts of migration

Migration affects both the country of **origin** (the starting point) and the **host** country (the end point) differently.

## A tale of two countries

Between 1950 and 1975, many people came from Jamaica to the UK. This had negative and positive social and economic impacts on both countries.

The social situation has now changed. Discrimination is illegal and equal rights are protected by law.
Ethnic groups add to the skills base and culture of the country, and now succeed in many areas of our society.

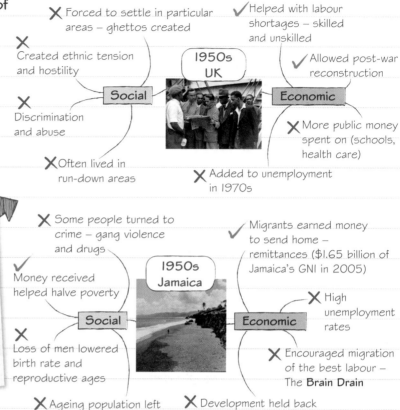

**1950s UK**

✗ Forced to settle in particular areas – ghettos created

✗ Created ethnic tension and hostility

Social

✗ Discrimination and abuse

✗ Often lived in run-down areas

✓ Helped with labour shortages – skilled and unskilled

✓ Allowed post-war reconstruction

Economic

✗ More public money spent on (schools, health care)

✗ Added to unemployment in 1970s

**1950s Jamaica**

✗ Some people turned to crime – gang violence and drugs

✓ Money received helped halve poverty

Social

✗ Loss of men lowered birth rate and reproductive ages

✗ Ageing population left as young moved abroad

✓ Migrants earned money to send home – remittances ($1.65 billion of Jamaica's GNI in 2005)

✗ High unemployment rates

Economic

✗ Encouraged migration of the best labour – The **Brain Drain**

✗ Development held back by loss of skill and enterprising people

## Worked example

International migration can have both positive and negative impacts. Describe the positive social and economic impacts of migration on the host country. Include an example in your answer. **(4 marks)**

FOUND'N **D-C**

Social – People learn about cultures in other people's countries. People from Poland can teach children in the UK.

Economic – They pick up the jobs that people in the UK don't want, such as fruit picking. This means they can make money.

There is a lot of text to be read for this question. Make sure you **highlight** the key words.

You must focus on the **host** country and describe the **positive** impacts.

## Now try this

HIGHER **A-A***

Choose a flow of population (migration) you have studied. Explain the social and economic consequences (impacts) of the migration on the country of origin. **(6 marks + 4 marks SPaG)**

Make sure you focus on the **country of origin**. Also, make sure your points are well supported and check your spelling, punctuation and grammar.

# Factors behind migration

## Push-pull mechanism

The decision to migrate is usually an outcome of push forces and pull forces.

- **Push** factors force people to move away – this will often result in **forced migration**.

- **Pull** factors encourage people to move – this will often result in **voluntary migration**.

Origin

Push factors

Migration

Destination

Pull factors

| Push factors | Pull factors |
|---|---|
| Harsh climate | Cheap land |
| Inaccessibility | No hazards |
| Divorce | Marriage |
| Ill health | Family ties |
| Unemployment | Plenty of work |
| Poverty | High wages |
| Heavy taxes | Good welfare services |
| Shortage of housing | Personal security |
| Civil war | Freedom of speech |
| Ethnic cleansing | |

Today **communication** is fast and direct. New technology such as the internet, and the media enable people to see what places are like without actually going anywhere.

This helps people make decisions about moving.

## 'Shrinking' world

Modern transport means people can move more quickly, efficiently and often more cheaply. Migrants can take advantage of improved transport networks:

- high-speed **rail** (the bullet train in Japan and links to the continent through the Channel Tunnel)

- major **motorways** and the relaxing of EU border controls

- larger and more powerful **aeroplanes** (Airbus A380) and new budget airlines (Easyjet, Ryanair).

## Government policies

- Open door policy – within the EU there is free movement between member countries. However some countries have put in place quotas to reduce the number of immigrants, e.g. Switzerland reduced from 6000 to 2000 the number of immigrants it allowed from the member states who joined the EU in 2004.

- Skills testing – the UK test *Life in the UK* can help assess a migrant's suitability to remain and work in a country. Australia also operates a points-based test.

## Worked example

HIGHER C

Explain the push and pull factors to suggest why an economic migrant has moved to the UK. **(3 marks)**

Pull factors will include the availability of jobs such as construction where pay will be better. Push factors will include poor health care or they have been forced to move due to damage caused by a natural hazard (earthquake).

The student shows a clear understanding of pull and push factors, and gives an example of each.

They are a good example of a low-skilled job, which helps explain the answer.

## Now try this

What does the term **push factors** mean? Give an example.     **(2 marks)**

# Temporary migration

Short-term population flow is also known as **temporary migration**. There is no permanent change of address, but both push and pull factors are involved.

## Reasons for temporary migration

**1** **EU increase in size**
In 2004, many East European countries (such as Poland and Estonia) joined the EU. Many people became **economic migrants**. Some workers are now moving back as the economic recession in their countries is over and prospects are better.

| Push factors | Pull factors | Issues |
|---|---|---|
| Unemployment | Job vacancies | 'Stealing UK jobs' |
| Low wages | Skill shortages | 'Milking UK benefits' |
| Poverty | Ageing labour force | No UK takers for low-paid jobs |
| Poor quality of life | Higher wages | Abuse and exploitation |
| | | Confusion with illegal immigrants |

Push and pull factors and issues for East European workers in the UK

**2** **Medical treatment**
Long waiting lists and high costs of private medicine have persuaded 100 000 UK citizens to become **medical tourists**, going abroad for treatment:
Not all medical tourism destinations are in HICs – India, Malaysia and Tunisia are also popular.

**3** **Sport**
In 1992 there were only 22 foreign footballers in the English Premiership.
Today there are well over 300. Players of other sports such as golf, tennis and Formula 1 racing also move around the world.

**4** **Tourism**
There are flows of people travelling to different parts of Europe on holiday, in particular from the colder north to the warmer south.

See also pp. 110–118
For more on tourism.

See also pp. 110–118

## Worked example

Complete the following sentences to describe the reasons for short-term migration. Use some of the words in the box below.　**(4 marks)**

| sporting | ~~cheaper~~ | permanent | longer | lower |
|---|---|---|---|---|
| | ~~shorter~~ | ~~higher~~ | ~~temporary~~ | |

Short-term migration involves a _____temporary_____ change of address. People travel abroad to have medical treatment as it is _____cheaper_____ than at home and waiting lists are often _____shorter_____. People also travel abroad for sporting reasons. For example, footballers are attracted to the UK by _____higher_____ wages.

### EXAM ALERT!

Even though this looks easy, make sure you don't use the same word twice and that you read the rest of the sentence after the gap.

Students have struggled with exam questions similar to this – **be prepared!**

ResultsPlus

## Now try this

Outline the factors that affect short-term population flows for medical reasons. Include an example in your answer.　**(3 marks)**

# Retirement migration

Retirement migration has become very popular with many elderly people in HICs. This decision is often taken because the elderly can now **afford** to make the move to an **environment** and **climate** that are more appealing to them.

## The elderly are moving because they

- no longer need to live near their place of work
- can downsize to a smaller house
- can use the extra money to supplement a pension
- want a quieter, more attractive environment.

## Consequences for the destination country

The advantages and disadvantages are:

- 👍 Increases in work opportunities in the geriatric sector – carers, nurses and doctors.
- 👎 Top-heavy age structure.
- 👎 Need to provide sufficient health, welfare and social services.
- 👎 Relatively high percentage of elderly people on the poverty line.

## Worked example

A warm welcome awaits YOU at...
**SHADY PALMS**
RETIREMENT RESORT
**Spain**
Relax in the private pool...
...or enjoy the many leisure facilities in the area including spas, fishing lakes - and a complete championship golf course!

**Difference in sunshine hours between Spain and the UK**

(bar chart: Hours of sunshine per month, y-axis 0–400, x-axis Jan–Dec)

☐ Malaga, Spain  ☐ Manchester, UK

Figure 1

Study Figure 1. It shows a brochure for a retirement resort in Spain. Suggest reasons why many people retire to areas such as Spain. **(4 marks)**

Spain offers up to 350 hours of sunshine per month, which makes it a great place to retire as people don't have to worry about being cold. Spain also has a wide variety of low impact sports, such as golf and fishing, which appeal to retired people. Retirement areas such as Shady Palms are equipped to cope with the elderly (e.g. stair lifts and wheelchairs) and so will encourage the elderly to move there.

### EXAM ALERT!

Most students used the resource well, but a few misread the question and gave reasons why people would retire to areas other than Spain.

Students have struggled with exam questions similar to this – **be prepared!**

## Now try this

Some people migrate overseas when they retire because:

☐ **A** they will miss their family in the country of origin

☐ **B** their place of work is in the country of origin

☐ **C** the climate is warmer in the destination country

☐ **D** there is a faster pace of life in the destination country. **(1 mark)**

# Types of 'grey' migration

## Types of retirement migration

Many elderly people in HICs are choosing to move during their retirement. There are three types of retirement migration:

- **local** – stay in the same locality but move house
- **regional** – stay in the UK but move to a 'more attractive' location
- **international** – move abroad, for example, Spain.

### Case study

You need to know a case study of the reasons for and consequences of retirement migration.

## Local

Many elderly people want to stay in their current location, so that they can live near their family. However, they often move to a smaller, more manageable house – this has resulted in the demand for **retirement apartments**.

Some elderly people move in with their children, or may move into a care home or hospice.

## Regional

Coastal towns such as Great Yarmouth, Worthing and Lytham St Anne's are very attractive locations for retired people.

These are sometimes referred to as **grey resorts**. They are equipped with transport, shops and health care to cope with a large proportion of 'grey' residents.

Popular retirement areas in England and Wales

## International (Spain)

750 000 Britons live out their golden years in Spain, attracted by the warm weather and leisure activities such as golf. But there can be negatives.

👎 Migrants may be forced to sell up and move back, often with no savings or property to fall back on. This is due to the strain being put on Spain's health care services, and language barriers leading to doctors' fears of being sued because of a wrong diagnosis.

👎 Spain has limited resources for the elderly as traditionally they are looked after in the family. Retiring abroad is different from going on holiday there.

## Worked example

What is a grey resort? Use an example in your answer. **(2 marks)**

Towns such as Eastbourne, Worthing and Lytham St Anne's are often called grey resorts. These are settlements which can cope with a large proportion of elderly people and so become popular areas for the ageing population.

## Now try this

Choose a study you have made of a retirement migration. Explain the reasons for this migration. **(6 marks + 4 marks SPaG)**

# Types of tourism

## Types of tourism

Tourism is one of the world's fastest growing industries. There are different types of tourism:

 **leisure, holiday, festival** – beach, city breaks, activity or adventure, health, heritage and cultural

 **VFR** – visiting friends, family and relatives

 **business** – meetings and conferences.

Tourism can be further categorised by:

 **destination** – local, national or international

 length of **time** – day breaks, weekends or longer periods.

The purpose, length and destination of tourism are interlinked. For example, people holidaying in long-distance destinations are likely to spend more time there.

### Measuring tourism

Tourism can be measured using different statistics or indicators:

- same-day visitors and overnight visitors
- international and domestic tourists
- inbound (to destination) and outbound (from origin) tourists
- tourism spending (£) per night or during trip
- % of jobs supported by tourism.

## In season

Tourism is also influenced by **seasonality**.

Trends:

- Business visits are evenly distributed throughout the year
- Leisure and VFR tourism dominated by school holidays – summer, half terms and Christmas

*Purpose of visits to the UK by season, 2012*

| | Jan–Mar | Apr–Jun | Jul–Sep | Oct–Dec |
|---|---|---|---|---|
| Holiday | 17% | 30% | 32% | 21% |
| Business | 23% | 27% | 23% | 27% |
| VFR | 21% | 25% | 27% | 26% |

☐ Jan–Mar ☐ Apr–Jun ☐ Jul–Sep ■ Oct–Dec

## Worked example

**HIGHER C**

Tourists visit places for different reasons – these can be for a holiday, business or to visit friends and family.

The divided bar graph shows the seasonal change in the percentage of visitors coming to the UK for a holiday in 2012.

Using the key and data from the table above, complete the divided bar graph.

**(2 marks)**

☐ Jan–Mar  ■ Apr–Jun  ☒ Jul–Sep  ◻ Oct–Dec

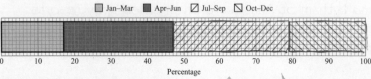

Percentage

> Make sure that you use a sharp pencil and a ruler. Take note of the shading in the key and use it appropriately.

## Now try this

**FOUNDN E**

Holidays are a form of leisure tourism. Give **three** different types of holiday.     **(3 marks)**

# Why tourism is growing 1

## Growing tourism

Tourism has grown drastically since the twentieth century, although some areas of the world experienced faster growth than others.

There are three main reasons for this growth – Social (people), Economic (money and business) and Political (government policies and intervention).

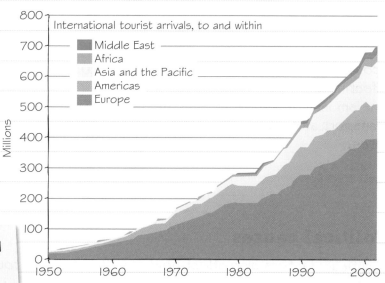

Growth of international tourism, 1950–2002

---

## Social causes

More days given for holiday – from 24 (2007) to 28 (2009) per year

Earlier retirement and more leisure time

Shorter working week – 50 hours (1950s) to 35–40 hours (2012)

Ageing population – increase in the 'grey pound'

Working conditions

Specialist holidays – e.g. weddings

Advertising on the internet

Communications and IT

Social causes of rising tourism

Changing fashions

Long-haul flights to exotic destinations – e.g. Maldives

Computerised and online booking systems

Companies can operate globally

Package holidays with flight, accommodation, food and drink all in one price

---

## Worked example

Explain the social reasons for the growth in tourism. **(4 marks)**

Tourism has grown because the working week has shortened. In the 1950s people worked an average of 50 hours compared with 35–50 hours today. This means people have more free time to pursue holiday and leisure activities. The ageing population in many HICs has increased and these people are spending their pensions on leisure facilities – called the grey pound.

This is a clearly written answer with excellent use of data, to exemplify the content.

---

## Now try this

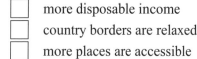

The list below outlines the reasons for the growth in tourism. Tick the **two** social reasons. **(2 marks)**

☐ shorter working week
☐ increased leisure time
☐ planes reduce journey times
☐ more disposable income
☐ country borders are relaxed
☐ more places are accessible

# Why tourism is growing 2

## Economic causes

Economic factors affecting the rise in tourism include wealth, transport and exchange rates.

Two-income families – 60% of women (2008) working!

Fewer children – 2.0 (1971) compared to 1.8 (today)

More disposable income (2008 £15 000 average salary) – more to spend on luxuries

Wealth

Minimum wage increased – £6.31 >21 years (2013) was £5.80 in 2009

Economic causes of rising tourism

Exchange rates

Changes in the currency for holidays

Huge changes in exchange rate in some countries e.g. USA

Transport

Journey times reduced

Long-haul flights more comfortable

New travel options – jumbo jets, cruise liners, cruiser coaches, high-speed rail

## Political causes

Political factors also affect how easy it is to be a tourist. Political causes include:

1. relaxation of border controls to encourage tourism – for example, EU countries allow **free movement** of EU members

2. attraction of the money to be made from visas and departure tax

3. reform – for example, dissolution of the Soviet Union (1991)

4. implementation of policies to enhance tourism – tourism in the UK provides 7.4% of all UK jobs and generates £115 billion.

Tourism is often supported by economic providers. In 2010, the World Bank gave $18 million to Sri Lanka's Sustainable Tourism and Development Project.

## Worked example

Explain the economic reasons for the growth in tourism. **(4 marks)**

Tourism has grown because people have more disposable income and holiday pay. In 2009, the minimum wage for people >21 years was £5.80, and in 2010 it increased to £6.08. Average salaries rose to £23 000 in 2008 and in 2007, people got 24 days paid holidays, but this increased to 28 days in 2009. This means people have more spare money to spend on luxuries such as holidays.

This answer has a good focus on the economic causes with useful support from data.

## Now try this

Figure 1

Look at the photograph.

Suggest reasons for the growth in tourism. Use evidence from Figure 1 in your answer.

**(4 marks)**

# Tourist destinations

A wide range of tourist destinations is now available, including independent hotels, guest houses, resorts, conference centres for business and cruise ships. Each tourist destination offers a range of attractions to suit different markets. For example, conference centres offer modern infrastructure and facilities designed to help business meetings.

## Factors

The factors that attract people to a certain type of destination can be **physical** (landscape and climate) and / or **human** (hotels, restaurants, temples).

**Physical**

- Physical landscape e.g. River Seine, Paris
- Bright, clear skies
- Beautiful scenery
- Slopes for all abilities
- Attractive landscape (e.g. Inca trail, Peru)
- Rapid water for sports (white river rafting) or mountains for bungee jumping
- Clean, sandy beaches
- Clear blue water
- Blue sunny skies
- Beaches popular
- Can be sunny or wintery (ski wedding)

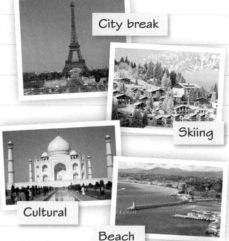
City break
Skiing
Cultural
Beach
Adventure
Wedding

**Human**

- Hotels nearby
- Good transport
- Built attractions e.g. Eiffel Tower
- Ski lifts, chalets and sport centres
- Famous landmarks
- Good transport
- Instructors for safety and support advice
- Proper safety and sporting equipment
- Hotels and restaurants nearby
- Deckchairs, water sports often provided
- Hotels and chalets nearby
- All parts of wedding covered – service, reception honeymoon

## Worked example

Figure 1

Look at Figure 1. It shows a holiday destination in the Mediterranean. Describe the physical and human attractions of the area. **(4 marks)**

The attractive scenery (hills) and the nice blue sky are obvious physical attractions. The sea is also nice and clear for swimming. There are local hotels nearby for tourists to stay in and facilities for sailing.

Remember to refer to physical **and** human attractions if the questions ask you to write about both.

## Now try this

Figure 2

Study Figure 2. Outline one physical and one human attraction of the area shown. **(4 marks)**

Don't write about the type of holiday in the photograph. Try to stick to the point and answer the question!

# The Butler model: Blackpool

Butler developed a model to show how any tourist resort might grow. He suggested that all resorts go through the same process.

**Case study**

You need to know an example of an EU resort and how it relates to the Butler model.

**Inter-war (1918–1939)** workers given **holiday pay**. Permanent population up to 150 000. Known as Europe's leading coastal resort.

**After WWII** most people had limited money to spend on luxuries like holidays.

**2003** huge development of casinos and conference centres. Hotels (Bond Hotel) refurbished and council began Talbot Gateway project to improve business sector.

Stage 6 Rejuvenation

Stage 5 Stagnation

Stabilisation

Decline

**1870s** workers granted annual holidays. Factories closed, and thousands visited. Tower, promenade, piers and arcade built.

Stage 4 Consolidation

**From mid 1960s package holidays** and cheap air travel encouraged travel abroad e.g. Mediterranean – for the 3 S's – sea, sand and sun!

**1990** the Sea Life Centre opened to help boost tourism but could not stop the decline.

**Early C19th** only wealthy could afford to visit. Blackpool still a hamlet.

Stage 3 Development

Stage 2 Involvement

**1846** railways provided cheap travel enabling working class to go on holiday.

Stage 1 Exploration

Number of tourists (y-axis) / Time (x-axis)

Blackpool and the stages in the Butler model

---

**Worked example**

HIGHER B–A

Using an example, outline the characteristics of the Development stage (stage 3) of the Butler model. **(4 marks)**

Blackpool went into the Development stage during the 1870s. Here tourism is beginning to become the area's main income. Attractions, such as the Tower, promenade and both piers, start to be built to help encourage people to visit. Workers were granted annual holidays so they had more time to visit. This was a help because factories had their own 'wakes week' in which they would close, allowing holiday time to visit resorts such as Blackpool.

You might include management of facilities mainly by locals, rather than large companies. Also the physical attractions of the area have yet to be compromised by the influx of tourists or the development of human attractions.

You don't have to use an example, but it helps!

---

**Now try this**

FOUNDN E–D

In stage 2 (Involvement) of the Butler model, the main attractions to an area are physical.

Tick **two** physical attractions from the list below. **(2 marks)**

☐ promenade    ☐ beach

☐ shops    ☐ sea

☐ pier    ☐ arcade

# The Butler model: Benidorm

Benidorm is one of the most famous resorts in the Mediterranean. Unlike Blackpool, Benidorm has only gone through **some** of the stages of the Butler model.

**Case study**

You need to know a case study of the development of an EU resort related to the Butler model.

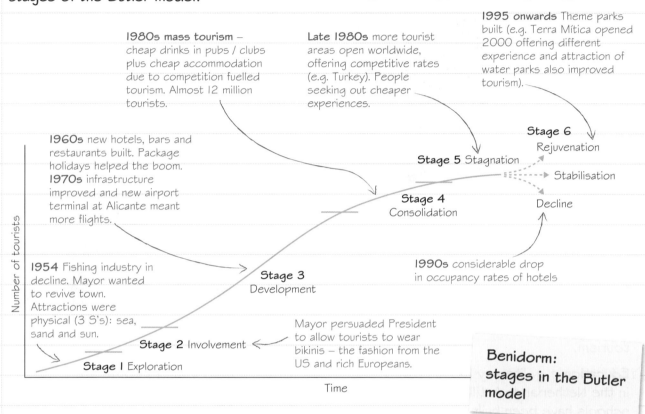

1980s mass tourism – cheap drinks in pubs / clubs plus cheap accommodation due to competition fuelled tourism. Almost 12 million tourists.

Late 1980s more tourist areas open worldwide, offering competitive rates (e.g. Turkey). People seeking out cheaper experiences.

1995 onwards Theme parks built (e.g. Terra Mítica opened 2000 offering different experience and attraction of water parks also improved tourism).

1960s new hotels, bars and restaurants built. Package holidays helped the boom. 1970s infrastructure improved and new airport terminal at Alicante meant more flights.

Stage 6 Rejuvenation

Stage 5 Stagnation

Stabilisation

Stage 4 Consolidation

Decline

1954 Fishing industry in decline. Mayor wanted to revive town. Attractions were physical (3 S's): sea, sand and sun.

1990s considerable drop in occupancy rates of hotels

Stage 3 Development

Number of tourists

Stage 2 Involvement

Mayor persuaded President to allow tourists to wear bikinis – the fashion from the US and rich Europeans.

Stage 1 Exploration

Time

Benidorm: stages in the Butler model

**Worked example**

**C**

Choose a study you have made of a holiday resort in the European Union. Explain how the resort has developed. **(4 marks)**

Benidorm went through the Exploration stage in the 1950s. It was a small fishing village with beaches, sun and sand. It became popular and new restaurants, pubs and shops opened (Consolidation). In the 1980s it went into decline as other destinations became popular and the number of people dipped. In the 1990s, Benidorm built water parks (Aqualand) and theme parks to help boost numbers.

Make sure you use some case study detail, such as specific dates, for stages, names of places and tourist data.

**Now try this**

**B-A**

Explain what happens during the final stage (Rejuvenation) of the Butler model. Use examples in your answer.

**(4 marks)**

# Social impacts of tourism

Tourism can bring both **positive** and **negative** social impacts to the tourist destination but not always in the same way. HICs often benefit more than LICs.

## Positive social impacts

👍 **Local crafts / products** can be sold directly, e.g. farmers can sell coffee to tourists for $20 a kilo.

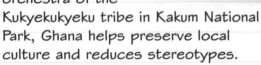

👍 **'Edutainment'** (education / entertainment); e.g. the bamboo orchestra of the Kukyekukyeku tribe in Kakum National Park, Ghana helps preserve local culture and reduces stereotypes.

👍 **Health** – life expectancy in Maldives has increased from 47 to 75 years between 1977 and 2004 because of the increased wealth made from tourism.

👍 **Education** e.g. literacy has improved in the Netherlands Antilles as more schools have been built with money made from tourism.

## Negative social impacts

👎 **Culture clash**, e.g. Islamic communities such as those in Turkey have strict dress codes so can be offended by clothes worn by tourists.

👎 **Loss of culture**, in Bali the significance of traditional cultures (such as religious dances) are lost through their use as tourist entertainment.

👎 **Seasonal employment**, e.g. employment in seaside resorts in England and Wales is an estimated 50000 higher in summer than in winter.

👎 **Tourists buying second homes** raises price of housing for locals, so young people are forced to move, e.g. in Appledore, Devon 40% of homes are now second homes!

## Worked example

HIGHER B-A

Explain the positive social effects of growth in tourism. Use examples in your answer.

**(4 marks)**

Revenue gained from tourism can be used to improve the health of local people. The infant mortality rate in the Maldives has reduced from 121 per thousand to 35 per thousand in less than 30 years. Tourism has also provided money that can be used in education. In Antilles in the Caribbean, the literacy rate has increased to 95% of the island, as they have been able to build more schools.

## EXAM ALERT!

This question looks easy, but many students fail to give examples in their answers. It is vital that you read the question carefully, and highlight the **command** words.

Students have struggled with exam questions similar to this – **be prepared!**

ResultsPlus

## Now try this

FOUNDN C

Describe **two** negative effects (impacts) that tourism has on the local people. Use examples in your answer.

**(4 marks)**

# Economic and environmental impacts of tourism

## Economic impacts

Tourism can bring positive and negative Economic impacts to a tourist destination.

**Positive impacts**

👍 **Employment**, e.g. 7.4% of UK employment comes from tourism. In the Maldives it is 57.6%.

👍 **National and local income**, e.g. in 2009 tourism was worth £115.4 billion to the UK and was 6.7% of the UK's GDP. In Kenya tourism is worth 13.7% of GDP.

**Negative impacts**

👎 **Leakage abroad**, e.g. an estimated 70% of spending by tourists in Thailand leaves the country and 80% in the Caribbean.

👎 **Enclave tourism** can limit employment and income to one resort or cruise ship so locals miss out. Around 80% of tourist expenditure goes to airlines, hotels and international companies.

## Environmental impacts

Tourism can bring positive and negative Environmental impacts to a tourist destination.

**Positive impacts**

👍 **Conservation**, e.g. in Belize, a departure tax of US$3.75 funds the Protected Area Conservation Trust which helps conserve barrier reefs and rainforests. Tracking permits in Uganda help protect gorilla habitats.

👍 **Raising awareness**, e.g. the La Tigra cloud forest visitor centre in Honduras is part-funded by eco-tourist dollars and is used by local Honduran school children.

**Negative impacts**

👎 **Habitat clearance**, e.g. deforestation of tropical rainforest to build resort enclaves like Thong Nai Pan in Thailand.

👎 **Overuse and pollution of water**, e.g. In Sardinal, Costa Rica locals demonstrated against a US$8 million pipeline drawing water from their local aquifer to supply coastal tourist resorts. Villagers would have been left without enough water for their basic needs.

👎 **Destruction of coral reefs** can occur through boating, diving, snorkelling and fishing.

## Worked example

HIGHER B-A

Explain the positive economic effects of a growth in tourism. Use examples in your answer. **(3 marks)**

The most obvious positive impacts from tourism are the increased availability of jobs, e.g. 8.3% of all jobs in the UK are created from tourism, and the increased revenue that can be made. In 2009, £115 billion was made in the UK as a direct result of tourism.

## Now try this

Explain the negative effects (impacts) that tourism has on the environment. Use examples in your answer. **(6 marks)**

Remember – the focus is on **environmental** impacts.
Make sure your spelling, punctuation and grammar are really good and that your points are clear.

# Eco-tourism

Many areas of the world are now encouraging eco-tourism – an eco-friendly form of tourism aimed at minimising the impact on the environment and benefiting local people.

**Case study**

You need to know an example to show how eco-tourism can protect the environment and benefit the local economy.

Educate tourists about how to act responsibly

Minimise the impact of tourism on the local environment and culture

Benefit local people by creating jobs and trade opportunities

Eco-tourism should...

Ensure tourists do not damage the local environment

Inform local people about why their environment is important

Help to conserve the local environment

Use resources sustainably

## Asa Wright Nature Centre, Trinidad West Indies

This nature centre was built by a non-profit organisation in 1967 on old plantation land. It aims to:

- leave plantation land to revert to rainforest
- **conserve** the valley so that wildlife is protected and for enjoyment of locals
- promote public awareness
- provide accommodation for visitors.

**Environmental** benefits

- only 10% of the area is accessible to visitors, the rest of the estate is left undisturbed to protect wildlife
- on-site recycling of refuse and waste water

**Social** benefits

- more than 50 staff live and work on the estate
- food is supplied by local growers giving employment for farmers
- staff get training and interest-free loans for building / renovation of homes

**Worked example**

What does the term **Eco-tourism** mean? **(2 marks)**

Eco-tourism is tourism which respects the environment and benefits the local community.

Make sure you learn the definitions of key terms.

**Now try this**

Choose **one** eco-tourist destination that you have studied. Explain how tourism has been managed to protect the environment. **(6 marks + 4 marks SPaG)**

Don't just list the strategies used. Explain how it protects the environment and link the content! Make sure you check your spelling, punctuation and grammar.

# Answers

## Geographical skills

### 1. Basic geographical skills

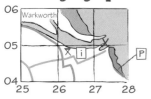

### 2. Cartographic skills

Include up to five points and use the data provided in the key to support your answers, ensuring you include the units. Points might include: it is wetter in the west; the highest rainfall is in the west of the UK; some places receive rainfall of over 1500 mm; the lowest rainfall of less than 625 mm is in the east of the UK; there is more rainfall in the north.

### 3. Sketch maps

1

| Feature | 4-figure grid reference | Symbol |
|---|---|---|
| Post office | 2345 | P |
| Telephone | 2144 | ( |
| Mast | 1944 | ↑ |

2

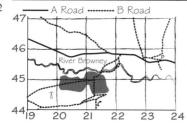

### 4. Map symbols and direction

1 Telephone.
2 North-west.

### 5. Grid references and distances

1 2 km (to the nearest whole number).
2 Mixed woodland.
3 112911

### 6. Cross sections and relief

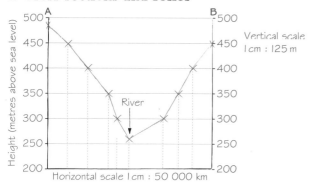

### 7. Land use and settlement shapes

Use evidence from the map to make your points, which might include: there are only isolated pieces of woodland; there are woods on the south bank of the river to the west of Sellack and next to the court at Baysham; there is a small plantation of mixed woodland at 565297; and another small plantation around the road junction at Pennoxstone.

### 8. Physical and human patterns

Settlement Y is located at a crossroads, therefore access is easy which would encourage nucleated settlements to develop. It is also located close to other larger areas of developments such as settlement Z, so settlement Y could be commuter area.

### 9. Human activity on OS maps

| Tourist facility | Symbol |
|---|---|
| Car park | P |
| Camp site/caravan site | ⅄ ⊞ |
| Tourist information | i |

### 10. Graphical skills

Try to make four points, making reference to the population graph. Points might include: Warkworth has 12% of its population below the age of 20, whereas England has 21% of its population below the age of 20; Warkworth has a 29% of its population above the age of 60, whereas England has 15% of its population above the age of 60; England has 5% more of its population in the 20–60 age groups; Warkworth has 17% aged under 30, whereas England has 30%.

### 11. Geographical investigation

It is a way of using technology through electronic displays to help understanding of the world. Examples of GIS are Google Earth, sat nav software or satellite maps.

## Challenges for the planet

### 12. Causes of climate change

Points might include: volcanic eruptions releasing large amounts of ash, which acts like a blanket and reduces the amount of solar radiation reaching the Earth's surface. You need to give a clear, well-structured answer, discussing two or more causes. Back up your points with clear and relevant case study examples.

### 13. The negative effects of climate change

Try to make your points with some explanation. Points might include the following.
* Rising temperatures could reduce crop harvests in key growing areas such as the wheat belts of the USA, Canada or the Russian Federation. This could then increase food prices and would mean that famine and starvation is more likely in prone areas, e.g. Sub-Saharan Africa.
* Rising temperatures could also impact on precipitation levels and this could effect crop harvests, e.g. rice crops in India would suffer.

### 14. Responses to climate change

Try to make three points with some explanation. Points might include the following.
* Some countries would be opposed to having targets set to reduce greenhouse gases such as carbon dioxide.
* Targets set for some countries are much higher than others. Industrialised HICs have higher targets compared to LICs, which can lead to perceived 'unfairness'.
* Some responses are expensive to implement.
* The restrictions would need to be fed downwards to industry and households. For instance, industries that emit large quantities of greenhouse gases would have to alter their practices to include expensive procedures such as flue gas desulphurisation.
* Some scientists have reservations about the extent of different impacts.

### 15. Sustainable development

You could have a variety of answers, e.g. park 'n' ride, cycle lanes, improved public transport, car sharing. For example: Cambridge has a park and ride scheme. This means that you can park your car on the outskirts of the city and get a bus into the centre. You do not pay to park your car, you only pay for the bus ride which use bus lanes to gain quick access to the city.
You need to give a clear, well-structured answer, discussing two or more examples of sustainable management techniques. Back up your points with clear and relevant case study examples. There are 4 marks available for SPaG so make sure that you use geographical terminology correctly and that your spelling, punctuation and grammar are really good.

### 16. Sustainable development: tropical rainforests

Examples of ways in which resource extraction from TRFs is being managed might include:
* replanting areas to re-establish habitats and species
* set up preservation areas/protect some species

- selective logging (clear-cutting is unsustainable and damaging to the eco-system)
- clean up oil spills and remove waste products
- conflict resolution between developers and indigenous groups
- ensuring biodiversity of an area is not lost
- establishing / protecting land rights of local people
- establishing education initiatives
- licensing only the companies that buy from sustainable forestry projects
- encouraging diversification from forestry to eco-tourism and crafts, to limit dependency on timber

You need to give a clear, well-structured answer, discussing two or more examples of sustainable management techniques and how these reduce the impacts of resource extraction. Back up your points with clear and relevant case study examples. There are 4 marks available for SPaG so make sure that you use geographical terminology correctly and that your spelling, punctuation and grammar are really good.

## Coastal landscapes

### 17. Types of waves

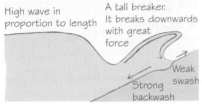

High wave in proportion to length

A tall breaker. It breaks downwards with great force

Weak swash

Strong backwash

Destructive waves have a high frequency (10–14 per minute) and short wavelength, producing a plunging, high-energy wave with a strong backwash which causes erosion.

### 18. Coastal processes and landforms

Points might include: loss of land through slumping; destruction of property; damage to sea defences; loss of animal habitats; potential for death or injury.

### 19. Erosional coastal landforms

Refer to processes and the sequence of events. Points might include:
- differential erosion due to perpendicular geology (reference to hard and soft geology that are perpendicular to the coast)
- harder rock is more resistant to erosion, therefore forms land which sticks out into the sea (headlands)
- softer rock is eroded (hydraulic action / abrasion / corrosion) at a quicker rate to form a bay
- an extension to sequence could refer to development of headlands into stacks / stumps or beaches within bays.

### 20. Depositional landforms 1

Try to describe three points. Points might include:
- longshore drift is the process by which beach material is transported along the coastline
- the direction of longshore drift reflects the direction of the wind
- longshore drift has a zigzag motion
- beach material is pushed up and along the beach by the swash
- beach material is pulled straight down the beach by the backwash.

### 21. Depositional landforms 2

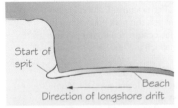

Start of spit

Beach

Direction of longshore drift

Include up to four points across your diagram and written answer. Points might include:
- movement of material along a coastline due to longshore drift
- occurs where there is a change in direction of the coastline
- over time the spit builds as more sediment is deposited offshore
- the spit may curve at its end due to action of wind and waves
- formation of salt marsh due to spit protecting area beyond it from wave action.

### 22. How coastal landforms change

Include up to four points, making reference to both fetch and geology. Points might include:
- the larger the fetch, the larger the waves
- therefore the approaching waves have more energy to erode
- softer rock will provide less resistance
- therefore increasing the impact of the wave energy and resulting in increased coastal recession.

### 23. Coastal flooding

Include up to four points, making reference to both prediction and prevention. Points might include:
- the Environment Agency monitors sea conditions to help predict potential flooding
- the Met Office forecasts the weather conditions that can contribute towards flooding
- sea wall defences and barriers can be built to prevent flooding
- avoid building on flood plains and river estuaries, or adapt building designs to survive flooding (i.e. building on stilts).

### 24. Coastal protection

Answer will depend on the example you choose, but make sure that you focus on the specific nature of the coastline and what management actions have been taken to protect it. You should examine both hard and soft engineering approaches. Try to explain your points well and use specific examples to support what you are saying.

### 25. Swanage Bay and Durlston Bay

**Advantages:** cheaper; environmentally friendly; aesthetically pleasing. **Disadvantages:** doesn't stop erosion; needs to be continuously maintained; less effective than hard engineering.

### 26. The Cornish coastline

Answer will depend on the example you choose, but make sure that you focus on the specific nature of the coastline and what management actions have been taken to protect it. You should examine both hard and soft engineering approaches. Try to explain your points well and use specific examples to support what you are saying.

## River landscapes

### 27. River basins

A tributary is a stream or river which flows into a main river, whereas a confluence is where two rivers actually meet.

### 28. Processes affecting river valleys

Include up to three points, making reference to the sequencing of features and the cause and effect links. Points might include:
- mass movement – relate to slumping, slides or creep
- saturation of ground
- lubrication along a weakness/plane in bank
- collapse into river.

### 29. The long profile

The discharge increases from the source to the mouth as more tributaries join further downstream making the river bigger. The depth of a river increases as it moves downstream and therefore the velocity of a river increases. This then enables the river to have more energy and can therefore transport more material.

### 30. Upper river landforms

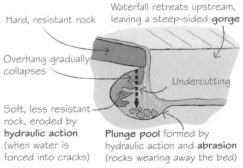

Hard, resistant rock

Waterfall retreats upstream, leaving a steep-sided **gorge**

Overhang gradually collapses

Undercutting

Soft, less resistant rock, eroded by **hydraulic action** (when water is forced into cracks)

**Plunge pool** formed by hydraulic action and **abrasion** (rocks wearing away the bed)

Include up to four points, either annotated in your diagram or explained in your written answer. Points might include:
- a fault in the geology exposes layers of hard and soft rock
- water pouring over the drop causes erosion of the softer underlying rock

- this leads to development of a plunge pool
- overhang of harder rock eventually collapses into plunge pool
- over time, the waterfall retreats towards the source forming a gorge.

## 31. Middle river landforms 1

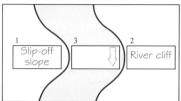

## 32. Middle river landforms 2

## 33. Lower river landforms

1 X = levee or embankment.
   Y = flood plain.
2 A levee is a raised embankment at the side of the river that helps prevent flooding. They are formed during flooding as heavy deposits are dropped near the river channel.
   The flood plain is the wide, flat area of land either side of the river and accommodates the flood water when the river overflows.

## 34. Why do rivers flood?

**Advantages:** sustainable; reduces the likelihood of flooding; trees will soak up the water (interception storage).
**Disadvantages**: can disrupt the wildlife; may not have the room to plant trees; loss of land for farmers; it is expensive.

## 35. River Stour, Dorset

Answer will depend on the example you choose, but make sure that you focus on the specific effects of flooding. Try to explain your points well and use specific examples to support what you are saying.
Points might include: damage to property; injury/death; disruption of transport; loss of power; contamination of water; crops destroyed; farm animals threatened; wildlife threatened.

## 36. Mississippi, USA (2011)

Make sure you focus on soft-engineering methods such as flood plains; setting aside land for water reserves, water storage areas or wildlife conservation; warning systems; preparation. You could give examples to support your points.

## 37. Reducing the impact of flooding

Include up to four points, making reference to both prediction and prevention. Points might include:
- the Environment Agency monitors river conditions to help predict potential flooding
- the Met Office forecasts the weather conditions that can contribute towards flooding
- reduce the impact within houses by design, for instance, placing electrical sockets up the wall and using water-resistant materials in the ground floor.

## 38. Flood management: soft engineering

**Advantages:** cheaper to install; environmentally friendly (or less damaging); aesthetically pleasing.
**Disadvantages:** doesn't stop erosion; needs to be continuously maintained; less effective than hard engineering.

## 39. Flood management: hard engineering

**Advantages:** natural-looking materials can be used (earth and grass) which blend in with the environment; prevents water overflowing into critical areas; protects valuable land on the floodplain.

**Disadvantages:** in extreme flood events, water can spill over the top; they can burst under pressure causing increased damage to the unprepared land behind the embankment; when built out of concrete can be very expensive and often aesthetically unpleasant.

# Tectonic landscapes

## 40. Earthquakes and volcanoes

Try to give three points and use examples from the globe when possible. Points might include: in chains/lines along plate boundaries (Pacific ring of fire); along edges of continents (western coastline of North and South America); along the centre of oceans (Mid-Atlantic ridge).

## 41. Plate tectonics

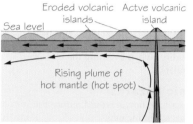

Volcanoes form over hotspots where magma is rising towards the surface due to the mantle plumes. At the surface, the magma erupts through the thin crust. These volcanoes often rise above the ocean surface to form islands. The Canary Islands formed as the crustal plate moved over the stationary hotspot.

## 42. Convergent plate boundaries

Points might include: plates moving together and collide; oceanic plate subducts the continental plate; fold mountains formed as plates collide; earthquakes generated from friction between subducting oceanic plate on the continental plate and there are explosive volcanic eruptions.

## 43. Divergent plate boundaries

Include up to three points, making reference to the sequencing of events and the processes that occur. Points might include:
- magma rises due to convection currents in the mantle
- this leads to pressure and doming of the oceanic crust
- magma rises through the weaknesses in the crust
- eventually (low viscosity) magma erupts onto the surface as a volcano
- the continued movement of plates pulls the boundary apart leading to more effusive eruptions.

## 44. Conservative (transform) plate boundaries

Include up to three points, making reference to the processes that occur at conservative boundaries. Points might include:
- plates slide past each other at conservative boundaries
- no crust is being destroyed or created
- there is no melted magma to become pressurised
- therefore, no volcanoes are created.

## 45. Measuring earthquakes

The focus is the point below the ground precisely where the earthquake originated from, whereas the epicentre is the point on the Earth's surface directly above the focus.

## 46. Living with hazards

Include up to four points, using descriptive reasoning. Points might include:
- earthquake-proofing of buildings and disaster planning makes people feel comfortable about the threat
- infrequency of earthquakes produces a lack of perceived threat
- often coastal areas, natural areas of high population density
- often major economically active areas, e.g. California for excellent employment and quality of life.

## 47. Chances Peak volcano

Answer will depend on the example you choose, but make sure that you focus on specific aspects of a volcanic eruption and how this effects both people and the environment. Try to explain your points well and use specific examples to support what you are saying. Points might include: injury/death rates; types of hazards presented; disruption of transport, power and communications; amount of displacement of people, animals and wildlife; long-term effects on ecology.

# ANSWERS

### 48. Bam earthquake (2003)

Answer will depend on the example you choose, but make sure that you focus on specific aspects of an earthquake and how this effects both people and the environment. Try to explain your points well and use specific examples to support what you are saying. Points might include: specific cause of earthquake; injury/death rates; types of hazards presented during the earthquake; hazards caused by the aftermath; disruption of transport, power and communications; amount of displacement of people, animals and wildlife; long-term effects on ecology.

### 49. Preventing tectonic hazards

Include up to four points, describing why it would reduce the effects of the eruption. Points might include:
- land-use planning to ensure settlements are not in the direct path of lava or ash flows
- barriers/ditches are in place to channel and divert lava flows
- emergency services and disaster plans are in place and well-trained
- cooling water sprays to solidify lava, preventing the lava from reaching towns or rich farmland.

### 50. Predicting tectonic hazards

Include up to three points, describing how it would reduce the effects of the earthquake. Points might include:
- seismometers measure earth tremors, which can help see if tremors are increasing in magnitude and frequency
- tiltmeters or satellite images can measure the movement of the ground to see if there is any pressure build-up
- gas detectors can measure if there are any changes in gas emissions that would indicate magma activity
- any early warning system would allow people to move away from the area or seek refuge in earthquake-proof buildings.

## A wasteful world

### 51. A world of waste

Include any two of the following points: high amounts of waste per person in HICs; due to larger disposable incomes; many products have large amounts of packaging; level of waste is falling due to increased recycling or increased awareness of the waste issue.

### 52. Wealth and waste

Include up to four points, explaining in each case why this contributes to high waste levels. Points might include:
- more disposable income
- purchasing more items
- tend not to reuse or repair, but replace with new
- therefore, old item and new packaging ends up as waste.

### 53. Domestic waste in HICs

Saving materials that can be reused again.

### 54. Recycling waste locally

1  C – Bexley
2  D – 16

### 55. Recycling waste locally: Camden

Answer will depend on the example you choose, but make sure that you have selected a local, not national scale. Focus on specific types of recycling and explain the process and impacts of each example. You need to give a clear, well-structured answer, discussing two or more examples of the recycling process and how recycled material is used. Back up your points with clear and relevant case study examples. There are 4 marks available for SPaG so make sure that you use geographical terminology correctly and that your spelling, punctuation and grammar are really good.

### 56. Waste disposal in HICs

Include up to three points, highlighting the differences between them. Points might include:
- landfill, where waste is buried in large holes
- incineration, where the waste is burned and can include recovering the energy to produce electricity
- recycling resources.

### 57. Non-renewable energy

Answer will depend on the example you choose.
**Advantages:** reliable and relatively abundant source of energy; still the most important fuels for power and transport systems; large economic benefit to the countries that possess reserves of fossil

fuels; technology is providing energy-efficient solutions.
**Disadvantages:** burning fossil fuels releases greenhouse gases, contributing to climate change; produces environmental impacts such as acid rain; environment damaged during drilling, recovery and transportation of oil through spillages and contaminated water supplies; resources are non-renewable so they will eventually run out.

### 58. Renewable energy

1  There are environmental concerns over wind farms interfering with migratory birds.
2  Points might include: green energy – does not exploit natural resources; does not release $CO_2$; once set up is relatively cheap to run; construction of turbines provides employment.

### 59. Energy deficit and surplus

B – use more energy than they produce.

### 60. Wasting our energy

Include up to three points. Points might include: leaving equipment on such as printers, computers, faxes; inadequate heat insulation; poorly maintained equipment; leaks and vibrations from machinery; heat wasted through exhausts and flumes; poor energy efficiency of machinery.

### 61. Carbon footprints

B – the amount of carbon used per person.

### 62. Energy efficiency

Answer will depend on the examples you choose. Points need to identify different examples of where energy is wasted in the UK. For each point, explain how the energy is being wasted and what could be done to reduce the waste. You need to give a clear, well-structured answer, discussing two or more examples. Back up your points with clear and relevant case study examples. There are 4 marks available for SPaG so make sure that you use geographical terminology correctly and that your spelling, punctuation and grammar are really good.

## A watery world

### 63. Water consumption

### 64. Rising water use

Include up to three points, giving a short explanation of each, or a comparison to water use in LICs. Points might include: good access to clean, safe water; use of many labour-saving devices for laundry and cleaning; personal sanitation is a high priority, therefore people shower/wash every day; greater level of tourism and leisure that requires high water usage.

### 65. Local water sources

Include up to four points, giving the sequence and short explanation of key stages. Points might include:
- aquifers are layers of rock below the surface which store large quantities of water
- aquifers become recharged when it rains
- water percolates through the soil and is trapped by impermeable bedrock
- the stores of water are extracted through drilling wells or boreholes or can rise by hydrostatic pressure
- examples include the Chiltern Hills, London or Australian Basin.

### 66. Water surplus and deficit

C – high rainfall and low temperatures.

### 67. Water supply problems: HICs

Include up to three points, making sure the points relate to the map and explore why water supply problems exist. Points might include:

- low annual rainfall in the south and east
- major cities are located here creating higher demand
- mostly arable agriculture, therefore high demand on water
- economically prosperous areas so high consumer usage, e.g. domestic appliances, leisure.

### 68. Water supply problems: LICs
Select two major water supply problems and explain the cause and effect of each example. Points might include:
- lack of water due to low rainfall areas
- collecting water is a major daily task
- lack of clean water causing diseases
- water sources becoming polluted through farming, industry and deforestation
- lack of infrastructure for storage, treatment and delivery of clean water
- also lack of separation and treatment of sewage and waste water.

### 69. Managing water in HICs
1 **C** – drip irrigation which waters plants when needed.
2 **D** – using a dual-flush toilet.

### 70. Managing water in LICs
Include up to four points, explain the methods used and give examples of places where the technology is being used. Points might include: cost-effective boreholes; water pumps; gravity-fed schemes; rainwater harvesting; sewage recycling for farming.

### 71. Managing water with dams
Answer will depend on the examples you choose. Points need to identify the water management scheme, explain why there is a need for it in that environment and describe some specific points of the scheme. You need to give a clear, well-structured answer, discussing two or more examples from your scheme. Back up your points with clear and relevant case study examples. There are 4 marks available for SPaG so make sure that you use geographical terminology correctly and that your spelling, punctuation and grammar are really good.

### 72. WRMS, Sydney
Answer will depend on the examples you choose. Scheme should be a water-management scheme on a large scale. Ensure you focus on the effects of the scheme, including the impact on the environment, people, economy, energy supply, travel, agriculture. You need to give a clear, well-structured answer, discussing two or more effects. Back up your points with clear and relevant case study examples. There are 4 marks available for SPaG so make sure that you use geographical terminology correctly and that your spelling, punctuation and grammar are really good.

## Economic change

### 73. Economic sectors
Include up to four points, using evidence taken directly from the graph to illustrate each point. Points might include:
- the primary sector of the economy has declined from 10% to 3% between 1970 and 2010
- the most rapid decline occurred in the 1970s
- the tertiary sector has grown rapidly during this period, from 30% in 1970 to 65% in 2010
- Country Z was an industrial economy in 1970, but is post-industrial in 2010
- the wealth of Country Z will have risen since 1970
- the primary sector continues to employ fewer workers, but mechanisation and automation are used to maintain output.

### 74. Primary sector decline
Include up to four points, explaining through examples when possible. Points might include:
- mechanisation and automation – the change from coal mines to open-cast mining that use large excavators to increase productivity
- globalisation – the ability to trade with the rest of the world
- exhaustion of resources – overfishing of the North Sea
- competition for workforce from the growth of other sectors – higher paid jobs in tertiary sector.

### 75. Secondary sector decline
1 **D** – a large company that operates all over the world.
2 Any relevant example – Coca-Cola, Nike, Shell, Apple, etc.

### 76. China (MIC)
Answer will depend on the examples you choose. In either case, describe several points that need to be present to grow the secondary sector.
For LICs, points might include: cheap and abundant labour; low land costs; government funding; foreign investment by TNCs seeking low cost supply for globalisation.
For MICs, points might include: cheap and abundant raw materials; skilled workforce; global expansion of trade; investment in R&D. You need to give a clear, well-structured answer, discussing two or more reasons. Back up your points with clear and relevant case study examples.

### 77. Tertiary sector growth 1
Include up to four points, explaining through examples and data when possible. Points might include:
- many people today have higher disposable incomes, UK average up from £12 000 to £13 500 since 1995
- people can therefore afford to spend money on luxuries such as iPads or smartphones
- more ICT and telecommunication services are provided – examples include: call centres in UK increase by 38 000 between 2006 and 2007; social changes such as DVDs at home, online streaming, satellite or cable.

### 78. Tertiary sector growth 2
farming; ageing; disposable; more; holidays

### 79. Location of industries 1
Economic development between 1980 and 2010 has resulted in fewer primary and secondary activities, but a growth of tertiary activities. Use references to the sketch maps to explain this change, points might include:
- closure of the coal mine and one of the steel works
- the timber yard has been replaced by a call centre
- the car plant employs fewer people, probably due to automation
- tertiary activities have grown (health club, supermarkets, nature reserve, call centre, etc.).

### 80. Location of industries 2
Clearly identify three factors and why it changes over time. Points might include:
- Good transport links making it easy and cost-effective to connect with customers and suppliers. However, roads become congested as populations and prosperity grows.
- Government incentives try to influence economic growth in depressed areas, which are then withdrawn when no longer required.
- Low land costs can attract industries, but land values then increase as the area becomes more wealthy.
- Improved ICT and telecommunications means tertiary and quaternary activities can choose their location.

### 81. Rural de-industrialisation: benefits
Include up to three points, giving descriptive examples in each case. Points might include:
- Reduce pollution and environmental impacts – slag heaps no longer dominating the landscape in former coal mining areas.
- Old industry buildings can be re-used for tourism sites either as heritage museums (e.g. Saltaire mills World Heritage Site), or re-used as other attractions (e.g. Eden Project).
- Convert former industrial housing into rural villages (e.g. Penallta, Wales).

### 82. Rural de-industrialisation: costs
Include up to three points, giving descriptive examples in each case. Points might include:
- Unemployment – large-scale job losses that occur when industries close increase costs of social welfare.
- Taxation is reduced as less tax is raised from industry and employees.
- Rural depopulation can occur as people move to urban areas to seek higher quality of life. This can leave an ageing population in the rural areas and result in closure of facilities such as schools.
- Decontamination costs for dealing with polluted former industrial sites.

## Settlement change

### 83. Settlement functions
1 The function describes what a settlement's principle purpose or activity is.

2  Strategic – the oldest part of the city are protected inside the river meander. This part of the city contains a castle and cathedral.

## 84. Change in rural communities

Include up to two points explaining the social impact of the points chosen. Points might include:

- Services can close down or become very limited, which in turn can lead to a spiral decline. For instance, the closure of rural schools means it becomes harder for families to live in these areas.
- Depopulation can change the demographics of the rural population, often resulting in an ageing population. This changes the level and type of services required in the area.

## 85. Changing urban areas

Include up to four points that illustrate how the changes to population structure can result in more flats being built. Points might include:

- population is increasing due to low death rates and immigration, meaning more houses are required
- families are less likely to live together than they were in the past
- younger generation move out to gain independence into affordable flats
- older generation retain independence but often downsize their homes
- higher divorce rates and longer life expectancy means more people are living alone.

## 86. Land use change 1

**Advantages:** close to city centre; popular area for employment and residential; plenty space so bigger houses; space for leisure facilities; cheaper to build.
**Disadvantages:** loss of countryside; increasing urban sprawl; puts pressure on existing services; often relies upon commuting leading to congestion and higher carbon emissions.

## 87. Land use change 2

Include up to four advantages, explaining the merit of each example. Points might include:

- located close to the city centre and all cultural and entertainment facilities
- can be cheaper to develop as utilities are often in place
- re-uses brownfield land, preventing urban decay
- population lives closer to employment so reducing commuting.

## 88. De-industrialisation

Include at least four consequences of de-industrialisation, giving examples and explanations of the impacts. Points might include:

- the old industrial landscape can rapidly become derelict
- dereliction can lead to increased levels of crime and social decline
- renewal aims to provide new employment in modern industries
- redevelopment can either rejuvenate old buildings or clear them away for new developments.

You need to give a clear, well-structured answer, discussing two or more impacts. Back up your points with clear and relevant case study examples.

## 89. Brownfield and greenfield sites

electricity; saves; employment; convenient; reduces.

## 90. Growing cities in LICs

Include two points, ensuring each one focuses on rural–urban migration. Explore how each one impacts on the area.
Points might include:

- A rapidly increasing population leads to limited access to housing and utilities. This can result in shanty towns (botis or favelas), as well as pressure on public utilities like clean water and electricity.
- New migrants from rural areas increases the competition for lowest paid jobs, leading to many ending up in the informal sector or black market.

## 91. Dhaka

Answer will depend on the example you choose. Describe several effects that are direct impacts of rapid urban growth. Brazil and Egypt are acceptable examples even though they are now MICs. Effects could include:

- Pollution: noise and air from the large number of congested traffic vehicles; or water due to industrial waste being dumped, or insufficient sewage systems to deal with the increased population.
- Housing: insufficient and inadequate housing leads to overcrowding and disease; shanty towns spring up on unused land that is often not safe for normal housing.

# Population change

## 92. World population

Include up to four reasons and explain each one with further details and possible example areas. Points might include:

- varied physical conditions across the globe so different carrying capacities
- mountainous areas can lead to a sparse population because of poor soil and/or challenging climate
- rich, fertile soils can support large populations
- coastal areas can lead to dense populations as they are a good location for trade and communication
- industrial areas attracts people as a workforce, as does tourism.

## 93. The demographic transition model

During Stage 3, the population continues to grow, but the rate of this growth starts to decline. This is because the birth rate starts to drop and the death rate continues to fall.

## 94. Birth and death rates

Include up to four reasons why the death rate declines in Stage 2 of the DTM. Explain each one with further details. Points might include:

- health care is improving, with vaccination programmes and better medical staff and facilities leading to higher life expectancy
- better access to safe water and good waste disposal has improved levels of hygiene and reduced disease
- improved health care and better hygiene leads to lower infant mortality rates.

## 95. Population in China

Include up to four reasons why the east is densely populated, explaining each one if required. Points might include:

- Physical factors: flat land mostly under 500 m above sea level, near rivers for abundant water supply with a temperate climate; whereas the west of China is dominated by mountains and desert, which only support lower population levels.
- Human factors: widespread economic migration driven by the pull of industrial jobs in the eastern coastal areas. These areas have excellent communication links, particularly large ports for international trade.

## 96. Population in the UK

The distribution of the UK population is uneven. Describe up to three factors that cause this variation. Points might include:

- There are two main areas of particular high density – the south-east and from the Midlands to the north-west of England. These areas are dominated by large cities where economic activity is the greatest (London, Birmingham, Manchester).
- Sparsely populated areas are located where relief is a prime factor such as central Wales (Snowdonia) and the Highlands of Scotland.
- Areas of moderate population density surround the densely populated areas and the regional cities mostly centred on the coast (Cardiff, Newcastle, Edinburgh).

## 97. Coping with overpopulation

Include a range of specific points for both incentives and disincentives that have been used, providing an explanation for each.
Incentives could include: cash bonuses or tax incentives; longer maternity or paternity leave; better childcare and free health care; preferred housing for families.
Disincentives could include: encouragement for contraception and/or sterilisation; fines; limits on the number of children per couple; loss of employment.
You need to give a clear, well-structured answer, discussing both incentives and disincentives. Back up your points with clear and relevant case study examples.

## 98. Coping with underpopulation

Answer will depend on the example you choose. Describe several techniques used by that country to have direct impact on the birth rate. Expand on the detail of each technique employed.
Points might include: cash incentives for having more than one child; longer paid maternity leave; paternity leave; child savings schemes; free or preferential education; free health care for mothers and child; better childcare; immigration policies; encouragement to avoid abortions and sterilisation.

### 99. Population pyramids: LICs
**1** LIC.
**2** The population pyramid has a wide base, showing a high birth rate. The top of the pyramid narrows rapidly indicating a relatively high death rate and low life expectancy.

### 100. Population pyramids: MICs and HICs
base; low; wider; death; expectancy.

### 101. Young and old
Include at least two points concerning a youthful population, specifying the consequences of each. Points might include:
- increasing pressure on the provision of services (schooling, health care, food supply and housing)
- higher proportion of the population is of working age, leading to increasing workforce and economic growth
- more people are dependent upon parental support.

### 102. An ageing population
Answer will depend on the example you choose. Describe several advantages of having an ageing population for that country. Expand on the detail of each advantage. Points might include:
- higher disposable incomes leading to economic growth through increased consumer spending
- increased demand for housing, leading to development in both rural and urban areas
- greater demand for retirement and healthcare services leads to improved provision.

## A moving world

### 103. People on the move
Refugees are people who have suffered from forced migration because of either persecution or war. Examples include Afghanis and Albanians.

### 104. Migration into and within Europe
An economic migrant is someone who moves to find employment.

### 105. Impacts of migration
Answer will depend on the example you choose. Describe several consequences relating to the country of origin. Points might include:
- Social impacts: ageing population as working-aged people leave; reduced birth rates as men migrate; money sent back helps remaining family members avoid poverty; rural depopulation.
- Economic impacts: 'brain drain' as most able leave; remittances help to increase consumer spending; loss of skills hinders the development of the next generation.
You need to give a clear, well-structured answer, discussing two or more impacts. Back up your points with clear and relevant case study examples. There are 4 marks available for SPaG so make sure that you use geographical terminology correctly and that your spelling, punctuation and grammar are really good.

### 106. Factors behind migration
Push factors are the reasons people move away from an area or country. Examples include civil war or ethnic cleansing, poverty, lack of employment, harsh climate or natural disaster, persecution or political change.

### 107. Temporary migration
Answer must relate to medical reasons with an example given. This may include: lower cost of treatment; better standard of health care; unavailability of specialist treatments; to avoid long waiting lists.

### 108. Retirement migration
C – the climate is warmer in the destination country.

### 109. Types of 'grey' migration
Answer will depend on the example you choose. Aim to explain potential push and pull factors that lie behind retirement migration. You also need to explain why people choose different locations for retirement. You need to give a clear, well-structured answer, discussing two or more management techniques. There are 4 marks available for SPaG so make sure that you use geographical terminology correctly and that your spelling, punctuation and grammar are really good.
Points might include: better climate; improved location; no longer tied to an area by employment; to be closer to family members; better leisure and social activities; smaller house ('downsizing').

## A tourist's world

### 110. Types of tourism
Different types might include: beach, cultural, heritage, adventure or activity, city breaks, health, festivals, educational visits, visiting family or friends, celebrations (weddings etc.).

### 111. Why tourism is growing 1
shorter working week; increased leisure time.

### 112. Why tourism is growing 2
Include up to four reasons. Points might include: beautiful scenery; adventure and activities including hill walking, sailing and fishing; camping/caravans for young families; improved transport links; higher disposable incomes.

### 113. Tourist destinations
Identify and explain one physical and one human attraction that would attract tourists.
**Physical:** good snow conditions on the mountains for skiing and other winter sports; a range of slopes for different levels of ability; beautiful scenery; good weather.
**Human:** abundant accommodation; provision of ski-lifts; restaurants, bars and cafes for night-time entertainment; ski-schools and mountain guides.

### 114. The Butler model: Blackpool
beach; sea.

### 115. The Butler model: Benidorm
Include up to four points and describe the relevance of each point to the rejuvenation of the resort. Points might include: investment in specialist developments (e.g. Terra Mitica); rebranding the resort to appeal to different groups of tourists; upgrading of facilities and accommodation; 'business' tourism (e.g. conferences).

### 116. Social impacts of tourism
Answer will depend on the example you choose. For both of the effects chosen, explain why tourism has a negative impact on the local population and give examples.
Points might include: cultural clash (e.g. beach holidays in Islamic countries); loss or dilution of local cultures and traditions (e.g. Bali or the Andes); housing becomes unaffordable due to tourists buying second homes; seasonal employment dominates; invasion of privacy.

### 117. Economic and environmental impacts of tourism
Include two effects giving a full explanation as why they have negative impacts on the environment using examples.
Points might include: loss of natural habitats for development and transport links; overuse of water supplies in hot, arid countries as tourism has very high water demands; increased pollution through traffic congestion, rubbish and sewage; over-use of natural attractions (e.g. coral reefs); loss of wildlife; loss of tranquillity.

### 118. Eco-tourism
Answer will depend on the example you choose. For your example, explain fully what management actions are being applied and how do these help to protect the environment. Give specific examples when possible. Points might include:
- working directly with the local community to protect the environment and preserving local cultures
- raising awareness and educating tourists and the local community so they contribute towards the conservation of the environment and do not cause unintentional damage
- re-investing some of the money gained from tourism into environmental projects
- identify particular environments that are critically in danger and prevent access, or make into nature reserves
- provide direct skilled employment to the local community
- encourage locally-owned tourism businesses.

Published by Pearson Education Limited, Edinburgh Gate, Harlow, Essex, CM20 2JE.

www.pearsonschoolsandfecolleges.co.uk

Copies of official specifications for all Edexcel qualifications may be found on the Edexcel website: www.edexcel.com

Text and original illustrations © Pearson Education Limited 2013
Edited, produced and typeset by Wearset Ltd, Boldon, Tyne and Wear
Illustrated by Wearset Ltd, Boldon, Tyne and Wear
Cover illustration by Miriam Sturdee

The rights of Anne-Marie Grant to be identified as author of this work have been asserted by her in accordance with the Copyright, Designs and Patents Act 1988.

First published 2013

16 15 14 13
10 9 8 7 6 5 4 3 2

**British Library Cataloguing in Publication Data**
A catalogue record for this book is available from the British Library

ISBN 978 1 446 90534 0

Printed in Great Britain by Ashford Colour Press Ltd.

**Acknowledgements**
The publisher would like to thank the following for their kind permission to reproduce their photographs:

(Key: b-bottom; c-centre; l-left; r-right; t-top)

**Air Images Ltd:** 65; **Alamy Images:** Ambient Images 39, ARGO Images 32, Chris Howes / Wild Places Photography 116l, Chris Pancewicz 87, David Gowans 1t, David Lyons 112, David R. Frazier Photolibrary Inc. 15, David Wootton 79, FLPA 19tc, Friedrich Stark 72, geogphotos 25, 31, Hikupic 69l, Jesper Jensen 70, Julie G Woodhouse 117t, Kevin Britland 21tr, Kevin Schafer 44, lowefoto 88c, Maciej Dakowicz 91, Matthew Oldfield Travel Photography 52, Mike Kipling Photography 88b, Nigel Cattlin 69r, OS Photography 80t, Stefano Ravera 56, Stephen Frost 18, The Photolibrary Wales 19bl, Travelmania 30; **Construction Photography:** Ashley Cooper 69c, BuildPix 55; **Corbis:** Reuters 49, Ryan Pyle 64, Skyscan 23c; **Courtesy of Google, Inc.:** 21tl; **Environment Agency copyright. All rights reserved:** 23l; **Fotolia.com:** Alexei Novikov 53, chrisdorney 81t, Jason Young 81tc, Lili Graphie 107b, 113t (Beach), Nikolai Sorokin 113bl, swisshippo 113t (Skiing), thanatip 80c, tonicarmona 113cl; **Getty Images:** Popperfoto 105c, Stone / Yellow Dog Productions 107t, The Images Bank / Nevada Wier 102cl, Time & Life Pictures / Winston Furtado 105t; **Les Bell Photography:** 1b; **MIXA Co Ltd:** 80cl; **NASA:** 50t; **Pearson Education Ltd:** Ikat Design / Ann Cromack 92bl, Jon Barlow 103b, Jules Selmes 85, 109, Lord and Leverett 78, 102cr; **PhotoDisc:** 113t (Wedding); **Photos.com:** 113t (Cultural); **Rex Features:** Daily Mail / James Gray 82, Gallo Images / Esa Alexandra 103r, Offside 107c, Photofusion 116r; **Science Photo Library Ltd:** Robert Brook 117b, Zephyr 50b; **Shutterstock.com:** Atlas Pix 24tr, George Green 24tl, Igor Koza 24cr, Neil Mitchell 20, wong sze yueng 98, Yobidaba 14; **SuperStock:** 113t (Adventure); **Veer/Corbis:** artjazz 92cr, Backyard Productions 19c, BartekSzewczyk 77cl, Corepics 80cr, Dmitry Kalinovsky 77t, icompass 108tc (Advert), Infinity 19r, kawing921 76, Monkey Business Images 108cr (Advert), somatuscani 108cl (Advert), trexec 83, Wavebreakmediamicro 77bl; **www.imagesource.com:** 113t (City break)

All other images © Pearson Education Limited

*We are grateful to the following for permission to reproduce copyright material:*
**Figures**
Figure on page 110 from http://www.visitbritain.org/insightsandstatistics/inboundtourismfacts/index.aspx Visit Britain

**Maps**
Maps on page 1, 2, 3, 4, 5, 6, 7, 8, 9, 25, 65, 83 from Maps International, Supplied by courtesy of Maps International and Ordnance Survey on behalf of HMSO, © Crown Copyright 2013; Map on page 58 from http://www.theclimatehub.com/uk-wind-farm-capacities-map, Department of Energy and Climate Change, Crown Copyright, Open Government Licence; Map on page 66 from http://earth.rice.edu/mtpe/hydro/hydrosphere/hot/freshwater/rainfall.html Earth Forum, courtesy the Houston Museum of Natural Science

Every effort has been made to contact copyright holders of material reproduced in this book. Any omissions will be rectified in subsequent printings if notice is given to the publishers.

In the writing of this book, no Edexcel examiners authored sections relevant to examination papers for which they have responsibility.